JUNE   MAY   APRIL

BOÖTES

LEO

Arcturus ★

Regulus ★

VIRGO

Spica ★

JUNE   MAY   APRIL

e lower edge of this map during the month indicated, and those nearly overhead appear at the top.

MAP OF NORTHERN STARS. Stars that you will see in the sky as you face north. Turn the map s
that the proper month is at the bottom: then the stars just above the name of that month will be du
north—just above the horizon at 9 P.M.

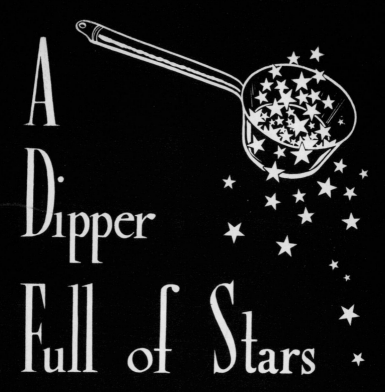

A Dipper Full of Stars

A Beginner's Guide to the Heavens

*by Lou Williams

Journal of Geology

FOLLETT PUBLISHING COMPANY

New York CHICAGO Los Angeles

Revised and Enlarged Edition

EDITOR: *Arthur Brogue*

PRINTED IN U.S.A.
By Photopress Inc., Chicago

Preface to the Revised Edition

The rapid advance in the science of astronomy in the past six years has made a revision of parts of this book necessary. The comments and suggestions of readers and reviewers, particularly Dr. E. S. Haynes, George A. Davis, Jr., and Edith Jones Woodward, have been most helpful.

I am especially grateful to my husband, Thornton L. Page, for his guidance and aid in this revision.

November, 1950   L. W. P.

Preface

> "Twinkle, twinkle, little star!
> How I wonder what you are. . . ."

We cannot help noticing the stars, nor do many of us fail to wonder a bit about them. With most of us it stops at the wondering stage, for the star maps seem mazes of dots and Greek letters. The language of the astronomy books is freely sprinkled with such meaningful terms that they are meaningless to us. The legends of ancient mythology are interesting, but how shall we ever find the star groups of which they speak? Often an interesting star formation catches our eye, but we do not know how to find its name and history.

In learning about the stars there is no better help than that of a friend who knows the heavens and is willing to teach you what he knows. How easy stargazing is then! We have tried to make this book the next best thing to such a friend. Each chapter is planned for one evening of stargazing. Our acquaintance starts off with the Big Dipper, because from it almost every constellation in the sky can be found.

If you enjoy the series of introductions contained in these pages — a broadening circle from our first starry friend, the Big Dipper — we hope you will not only keep in touch with all these friends, but will go on and become more familiar with the evening skies. We hope, too, that you will never look for new stars without noticing the old ones in their changed positions.

We trust that by the time you finish *A Dipper Full of Stars* you will feel eager and ready to tackle the most complicated sky chart and to absorb the contents of the astronomy books. They are really fascinating! This little book can be your passport to them.

The author is pleased to acknowledge her great debt to Mrs. Jessie Rudnick, formerly of McDonald Observatory, Fort Davis, Texas, who sketched most of the diagrams of the constellations and who made many valuable corrections and suggestions; to M. K. Hansen, for his services rendered in drafting the illustrations; to the University of Chicago Press and Yerkes Observatory, for photographs used as illustrations; to McGraw-Hill Book Company, for permission to quote from *Man and the Stars,* by Harlan T. Stetson; to D. Appleton-Century Company and Harper & Brothers, for permission to use material from books published by them; and, for their encouragement and assistance, the author wishes to express her appreciation to her parents, to Mabel Stearns, to Dr. Bertha Chapman Cady, and to Marie E. Gaudette of the National Staff of Girl Scouts Inc.　　　　**L. W.**

Contents

ILLUSTRATIONS

A Dipper Full of Stars

"*To acquire some appreciation of the meaning of the skies one must make the friendship of the stars; watch their majestic march through the night, and the slow seasonal advance of constellation after constellation from east to west throughout the year. To know Orion, Sirius, Taurus, and the Pleiades as leading roles of the winter skies; or Lyra, with its Vega, Cygnus, with its Northern Cross, Scorpio, and Antares as the quieter leaders of the softer skies of summer, gives one a sense of kinship with nature which makes a knowledge of their movements more significant, and even life a bit more worthwhile.*"

—HARLAN T. STETSON, *Man and the Stars*

1. We Meet the Dipper

Once you have made the acquaintance of the Big Dipper, it will introduce you to many of its friends in the sky. It is a star group to which few of us need an introduction, for most of us have been able to see it since we were very young. For most of us in the Northern Hemisphere, it is always ready to do the honors, for it never leaves the heavens. Any hour of the night, any night of the year, it is there for you to see. It may take a great many evenings of stargazing to meet all the Big Dipper's friends. But, as a great stargazer once said: "When you have done it, you will feel amply repaid for your exertions and you will have made for yourself silent friends in the heavens that will beam kindly on you, like old neighbors, on whatever side of the world you may wander."

Fig. 1.—The Big Dipper.

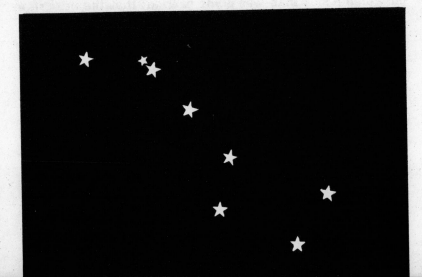

The Big Dipper itself is very interesting. Let us look at it again and learn more about it. Over in the north it shines, looking down on us in a very friendly fashion. Can you see a tiny extra star above the second star in the handle, counting from the end? If so, according to the Arabs of long ago, you have extremely good eyesight, but according to modern standards all you can conclude is that your eyesight is not poor! For most people with average eyesight can distinguish the two when they have favorable conditions for stargazing—that is, a clear atmosphere, absence of bright city lights, not too much moonlight, and the stars not too close to the horizon.

Whether the star became brighter in later years or whether we have better eyes than the Arabs, we do not know. We call the stars Mizar and Alcor, and some have called them the "horse and rider." The American Indian legends about the Big Dipper feature these two stars. Evidently the Indians, too, had no trouble in seeing both of them. The Indians did not refer to this star group as a dipper, but they interpreted it in other ways. Some tribes said that the four stars in the bowl were a stretcher on which a sick man was being carried; that the next star in the handle was the medicine man; that the next star was the medicine man's wife, and Alcor a tiny papoose on her back; and that the end star in the handle was a dog belonging to the medicine man's wife.

Other Indian tribes had more elaborate legends. One tells of a tribe which enjoyed plenty of game and hunting until a great bear came and frightened all the wood creatures away, ruining the hunting. Before long, famine

2

spread among the people. The three sons of the chief decided they would hunt the bear and rid their tribe of this evil. All through the summer they trailed him, but without success. Farther and farther north went the bear; close at his heels were the hunters, but it seemed they never could come near enough to shoot. Finally, when they were chasing him up a high mountain, they overtook him and shot their arrows. The bear jumped from the top of the mountain into the sky. The hunters, having concentrated so long on their chase, followed him into the sky, as if it were the natural thing to do.

Now each night we can see them still chasing the bear. For the bowl of the Dipper is really the bear; the first star in the handle is the hunter with the bow and arrows ready to shoot him. Next comes the second brother. He carries a kettle in which they hope to cook the bear. Alcor, of course, is the kettle. The third brother appears at the end of the procession carrying sticks for the fire and, we hope, some flint! Every autumn, so the legend tells us, they almost catch the bear. The heat of the chase melts his fat, and it falls to earth, coloring the autumn leaves yellow. Finally an arrow reaches its mark, and red is added to the fall coloring. During the winter months the bear recuperates sufficiently to allow the summer chase to go on as before, so that there may be colored leaves again in the autumn.

Fascinating as are the legends by which primitive folk made the stars seem less awe-inspiring, even more thrilling are the things which modern science finds out about them. Stars are not tiny points of light, nor are they jewels

3

embedded in the sphere of the sky, as the ancients thought. Neither are they "the windows of heaven," as the popular song writers say. They are actually suns. The stars which have been measured vary in size from giants, which have volumes many millions of times that of our sun, down to dwarfs about the size of the earth. Our sun is an average star of average size, but it would take more than a million planets the size of the earth to equal the volume of the sun. The stars appear as points of light because of their immense distances from us, hundreds of thousands, or much more often, millions of times the distance of the earth from the sun.

The distance between Mizar and Alcor is about 16,000 times the distance from the earth to the sun. Mizar and Alcor have been found to be not two stars, but six! Mizar was seen through early telescopes to be two stars. (It was the first double star ever seen through a telescope.) Later each of these was found to be really two stars. And yet, because of its great distance from us, it appears to us as one star. Later, also, little Alcor was found to be a double star.

Stars are said to be "fixed," because to the naked eye there has been little change in their positions *relative to each other* during historic time. This is not because the stars are motionless, but because they are so far from the earth that, although each is moving in its own course at high speed, it takes many thousands of years for their motions to alter their apparent arrangement in the sky.

For instance, the stars making up the Big Dipper are a group of suns each with its own motion. Slow though their motion appears to be, it can be detected and measured over a very long period of time. If we could go back 2,000 years to the beginning of the Christian era, we should probably see no difference in the shape of the Dipper. But if we went back 40,000 or 50,000 years, it would look very different. And if the interval were increased

FIG. 2.—a) The Big Dipper as it is today.
   b) The Big Dipper as it is today, with arrows showing amount and direction of motion of the stars in the next 100,000 years.
   c) The Big Dipper as it will look 100,000 years from now, due to this motion.

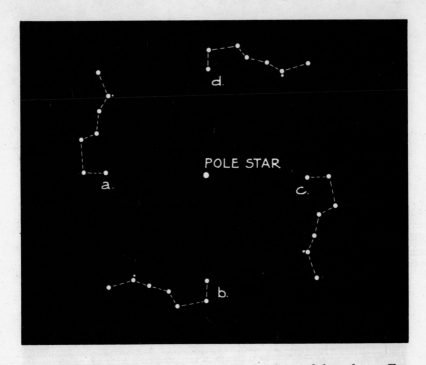

FIG. 3.—The Big Dipper at successive positions around the polestar. For May 5 they are: *(a)* 2 A.M., *(b)* 8 A.M., *(c)* 2 P.M., *(d)* 8 P.M. For June 20: *(a)* 11 P.M., *(b)* 5 A.M., *(c)* 11 A.M., *(d)* 5 P.M., etc. At 9 P.M. on July 20, the Big Dipper is in position *a;* at 9 P.M. on October 20, it is in position *b;* at the same hour on January 20, in position *c;* and in position *d* at the same hour on April 20.

to 100,000 years, the star group would be unrecognizable.

The Big Dipper is really the largest clock we have! The hunter legend tells us that the bear is being chased around the northern sky. Observe the Dipper some night for about three or four hours. You will see that the constellation as a whole seems to be slowly moving. It is, in reality, a giant clock hand on a twenty-four hour dial. Unlike an ordinary clock, the hand moves backward. Also unlike other clocks, the Big Dipper "hand" is not in the

6

same position each night at the same hour. There are some people so familiar with the position of the Big Dipper at any hour of the night throughout the year that they can determine the hour from its position. We cannot expect to be so accomplished at first, but if we acquire the habit of glancing at the Dipper now and then, remembering that each night it reaches a given position about four minutes earlier than it did the night before, we too shall soon be able to use this clock.

Having just said that the stars do not move appreciably, it probably sounds contradictory when we say that the constellation of the Big Dipper moves with such regularity that we may use it as a clock. The constellation of the Big Dipper only *appears* to move in the sky. This is also true of all the other star groups. Have you ever had the experience of looking from the window of a moving train and suddenly feeling that you were stationary and that everything outside was moving rapidly? We on the rapidly rotating earth get the impression that we are standing still and that the stars are moving. In reality it is we who are moving and the stars which are standing still (except for the barely observable motion mentioned above).

The rotation of the earth is the cause of the apparent movement of the stars during the course of the night. But how do we explain the fact that the Dipper always assumes each position a bit earlier than it did the night before? To explain this, we must remember that the earth not only rotates on its axis once every twenty-four hours, but that it is moving in an almost circular path, or orbit, around the sun. This movement constantly changes our position in respect to the stars, taking us along our orbit at a rate that causes the stars to reach the same position two hours earlier each month. Therefore, the Big Dipper appears in the same position on July 1 at 9 P.M. as it did on June 1 at 11 P.M.

Besides being a timepiece, the Big Dipper provides a convenient yardstick for measurements in the sky. Distances there cannot be measured in terms of our usual systems. An inch, a foot, or a meter means nothing. The heavens present the appearance of a half sphere viewed from the inside. The horizon is a circle and therefore measures 360 degrees, while the half circle from one horizon to the zenith (the point directly overhead at any locality) and down to the opposite horizon measures 180 degrees. The space between the two stars forming the side of the Dipper opposite the handle happens to measure a little more than 5 degrees. When you are pointing out stars, this is a good measurement to use.

These two stars in the bowl of the Big Dipper opposite the handle are known as the Pointers, for they point almost straight to the polestar, or Polaris, no matter what the position of the Dipper. Follow the direction indicated

FIG. 4.—The Big Dipper is the "yardstick of the sky."

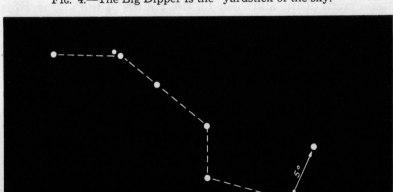

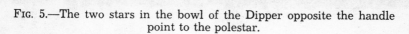

Fɪɢ. 5.—The two stars in the bowl of the Dipper opposite the handle
point to the polestar.

by a line connecting these two stars and extending about
five and one-half times as far beyond them, or about 28
degrees, and you arrive at Polaris, the North Star.

Is Polaris as bright as you had thought? Did you not
expect that a star with all the distinction of this one would
be larger and more important looking? It is much more
interesting than its appearance would indicate, for it is
the only star in the sky that never seems to move. The
axis of the earth points almost straight to Polaris, and if
that imaginary axis were prolonged, it would touch the
north pole of the sky—"the pivot on which the celestial
sphere seems to revolve."

The star appears stationary, and the other constellations
seem to move around it. But you can easily prove that

9

Yerkes Observatory

Fig. 6.—Photographs of star trails. Left, as they appear near the north pole of the sky; and right, near the Celestial Equator. The bright arc near the center of the photograph on the left is the trail of Polaris.

the polestar is not at the exact north pole of the sky by doing a bit of celestial photography with an ordinary camera. Open the diaphragm as wide as possible, and focus for distant objects. Point the camera toward the polestar, supporting it firmly in that position, and expose the film for a half hour or more. The developed negative will show lines partially encircling the pole. These are the images of star trails caused by the movement of your camera as it rotates with the earth. You will note that Polaris has described an arc of a very small circle, while the other stars have described arcs of larger circles.

After taking such a photograph, you may wonder how astronomers can make telescopic star pictures which are real star images and not merely trails. This is done by delicate machinery on the telescopic camera which shifts the instrument at the same rate as the star appears to move in the sky, and thus keeps star and camera always in the same relative positions.

A stargazer at the North Pole, instead of looking near the horizon for Polaris, would look straight up. As we travel north, the polestar seems to rise higher and higher in the sky. Actually, the latitude of any place in the Northern Hemisphere is equal to the number of degrees Polaris is above the horizon at that point. In Chicago, where the latitude is 42 degrees, the polestar is 42 degrees above the horizon. At the North Pole, latitude 90 degrees, the polestar is directly overhead. Just north of the equator Polaris is barely above the horizon.

Here is some practice with the "yardstick of the sky." With the help of the Big Dipper, see if you can measure

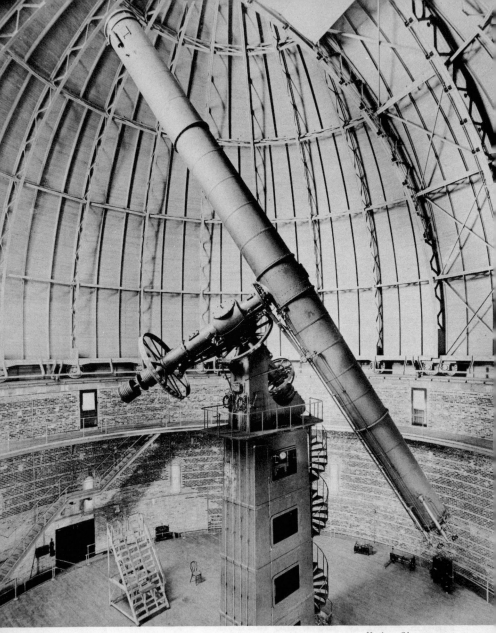

Fig. 7.—The 40-inch refracting telescope of the Yerkes Observatory.

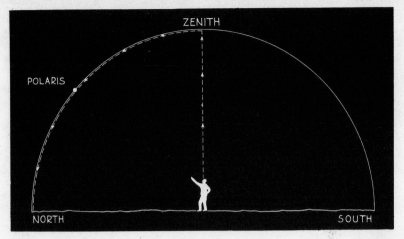

FIG. 8.—Observer finding true north by following straight down from the zenith through Polaris to the horizon.

from the horizon to the polestar and estimate your latitude. Then look it up in an atlas or on a globe and see how nearly right you were. In locating the horizon make allowance for any mountains which may intervene.

The polestar has probably done humanity more service than any other star, with the exception, of course, of our sun. Many a ship has steered its course by it, many travelers have found their way with its help. In the lines:

> ". . . . he traveled far,
> The sun his guide by day,
> And then by night a star . . . ."

the star meant is probably Polaris. In order to find true north, we have merely to draw an imaginary quarter circle from the zenith, the point directly overhead, through the polestar, and down to earth. This will give the approximate location of true north. Having done this, we can easily find the other points of the compass.

If you were lost in the Northern Hemisphere, you could tell in what direction you were going and in what latitude you were by the polestar, which you could find with the help of the Big Dipper. From the Big Dipper you could tell time, and be encouraged by seeing a familiar object.

The polestar is the end star in the handle of the Little Dipper. This is, supposedly, one of the most difficult constellations in the sky to make out. But do not be discouraged, for you will probably locate it on the first attempt. The best plan is to take a good look at the picture of the star group. Remember that the handle curves away from the polestar, *up* from it in the early evening in summer, and *down* from it in the early evening in winter. When one first looks at this constellation, he will probably see

Fig. 9.—The Big Dipper and the Little Dipper. Turn the book about until the Big Dipper assumes its proper position in the sky for the time you are observing it. When you do this the Little Dipper, too, will assume its correct position.

only three stars; the polestar and the two stars in the bowl opposite the handle, called the "Guardians of the Pole." Then, as one watches, the others seem gradually to come into view—and, lo and behold, you have found one of the most difficult constellations in the sky! Just remember that the Dippers pour into each other, and as they move around the polestar you will not confuse them.

Draco the Dragon, or, as it is sometimes facetiously called, "Draco the Snako," is the next constellation we shall meet. It is easy to find, although by including more or fewer near-by stars there are several possible interpretations of its outline. The one which seems most lifelike, and which is the usually accepted version, is shown in Figure 10. To find it, we look for the single line of stars winding between the Big Dipper and the Little Dipper; follow this line as it bends toward the Little Dipper and then away from it; and, finally, add to it the four stars in a polygon making up the dragon's diamond-shaped head.

Now we have made three new friends in the sky, friends who will always be twinkling down on us. For in the northern part of the United States these three constellations are circumpolar, a word meaning literally "around the pole." The circumpolar constellations for a given latitude are those that never sink below the horizon, but can be seen on any night, no matter what the date or hour. Of course, they are in the sky at all hours of the day and night but are naturally invisible in daylight.

If you look through the inside of a tall, dark chimney or smokestack some day, you may be able to see a few of the brightest stars then in the sky. This is because

15

FIG. 10.—The Big Dipper, the Little Dipper, and Draco the Dragon (as seen in the early evening in September). Turn the book about until the Big Dipper assumes its proper position for the time you are observing it. When you do this, the other two constellations will also assume their proper positions.

the smokestack cuts out some of the blue light entering the eye from the whole sky and makes the contrast between star and sky more noticeable. But even though the circumpolar constellations are always in the sky by day or night it is unlikely that you would see any circumpolars through a chimney in the daytime. For the north-

16

ern circumpolars, you remember, are always in the north, and through a chimney you could see only those stars which are directly overhead. Anyway, it is far simpler to look at the stars at night!

We are rather lucky to be able to see these circumpolar constellations, for they are at all times invisible in the southern part of the Southern Hemisphere. Likewise, we never see the stars near the south pole of the sky. The south pole of the sky is the point in the heavens directly above the South Pole of the earth. There is no star at this point, so there is no "South Star." But, though we cannot see the southern polar stars and many inhabitants of the Southern Hemisphere cannot see our polar constellations, we share a great many of the star groups farther from the poles of the sky.

It seems fitting that the three constellations we have mentioned should be considered together, and so they were by the ancient Greeks, who connected a great many of the stars with the affairs of their gods and goddesses. To them, the sky was a sort of historical and religious picture book.

They explained the presence in the sky of the Great and Little Bears (the constellations that contain the Big and Little Dippers) by the following legend. Callisto was a Grecian woman who had a beautiful little son called Arcas. Juno, queen of the gods, did not like Callisto. Though Jupiter did not share his wife's dislike for the woman, he was unable to change her opinion. Finally, Juno changed Callisto into a bear.

For years poor Callisto wandered about the woods. Her

little son Arcas grew up and became a famous hunter. One day when he was out with his bow and arrow, a huge bear crossed his path. Of course, it was Callisto. Arcas, not knowing it was his own mother, raised his bow to shoot. At that moment Jupiter happened to look down from Olympus. His eagle eye took in the situation at a glance. Quickly he changed Arcas, too, into a bear. Then he reached down, picked up Callisto and Arcas in one swoop, and put them in the sky. In his hurry, he grabbed the bears by their tails, and as he swung them into the heavens they began to stretch and stretch until they became unnaturally long for bears' tails. Callisto landed in the sky as the constellation of the Great Bear, her tail corresponding to the handle of the Big Dipper.

Between the figures of the Great and Little Bears lies the winding, sinuous form of Draco the Dragon. There are many legends about the sky dragon. One of them tells that it is the dragon that guarded the golden apples of the Garden of the Hesperides. Another tale is that Draco is the sleepless dragon that guarded the Golden Fleece of Jason's quest. Night after night you can see them now—the Great and Little Bears, with Draco curving between them, as they move around the polestar.

Having found the Big Dipper, can you make out Mizar and Alcor? Can you follow the direction of the Pointers straight to the polestar? From there can you see the Little Dipper curving from the polestar? Can you make out the head of Draco the Dragon, and then follow its winding body? Then you have accomplished a great deal for one evening of stargazing!

2. Following the Dipper's Lead

The next evening that we go out to see the stars, let us start again with the Big Dipper and allow it to introduce us to a few more of its companions. If the time is between early spring and late summer, and if we follow the curve of the handle of the Big Dipper on for about thirty degrees from the last star, we come to Arcturus, a bright orange-colored star.

You notice immediately, do you not, that it is brighter than any of the stars we looked at in the preceding group? Along with the other 19 brightest stars in the sky, Arc-

Fig. 11.—Follow the curve of the handle of the Big Dipper to Arcturus.

19

turus is of the first magnitude. Magnitude refers only to the apparent brightness of the star and not to its real size. For a star actually much larger than any that we call first-magnitude might be so far away that it would seem very tiny to us. First-magnitude stars are two and one-half times as bright, on the average, as those of the next group, which are called stars of the second magnitude. Examples of second-magnitude stars are the polestar and those of the Big Dipper, except Alcor and Megrez (the star which joins the handle of the Dipper to the bowl). In the whole sky there are 65 stars of the second magnitude. They are about two and one-half times as bright as stars of the third magnitude, of which there are 190 (among them Megrez). Similarly, the third-magnitude group contains stars about two and one-half times as bright as those in the fourth magnitude (which includes Alcor). And so on. It will be noticed that there are, roughly, three times as many stars in each magnitude as in the one preceding it.

Only stars belonging to the first six magnitudes are visible to the unaided eye: about 5,000 stars, only half of which are above the horizon at any one time. We have often heard the opinion expressed that the stars of the sky are countless. An exaggeration surely! For there are less than 2,000 to 2,500 stars which we have any chance of seeing at one time with our eyes alone. A very slight haze or bright moonlight materially lessens this number, and in addition many stars are too near the horizon to be seen. On average moonlight nights an observer will do well to see more than 300 stars at one time.

The orange-colored Arcturus, sixth brightest star in the sky, is the fourth brightest visible from most of the United States. Astronomers tell us that it is about 25 million miles in diameter—so big that we cannot really conceive of its size! And yet many of the other stars are as large as Arcturus or larger. They appear small to us because they are so far away. Our own sun, 864,000 miles in diameter, is too small to make a conspicuous appearance among the other stars. From the nearest star visible to the naked eye, Alpha Centauri, it would appear of average first magnitude, and, if viewed from that star, the sun would appear as a bright star in the constellation Perseus. However, from the distance of most of the stars, our sun would probably be invisible to the naked eye, and even as seen from most of the nearer ones could only rank as a fifth- or sixth-magnitude star, unnoticed except by the star-charting astronomer.

In the spring of 1933, rays from Arcturus turned on the lights at A Century of Progress Exposition in Chicago. The switch that opened the Fair started by the touch on a photoelectric cell of a light beam from Arcturus. Why was Arcturus chosen? Not for its brightness alone, or the fact that it is a conspicuous star in the springtime sky, but chiefly because of its *distance* from the earth.

Although the stars appear to be scattered over the surface of the sky, actually they are at different distances from the earth. Because they are enormously far from each other and from the earth their distances cannot be expressed easily in miles. So astronomers use a larger unit of measurement for star distances, the *light-year*. A light-year is the *distance* that light, moving at its constant rate of 186,000 miles *per second,* travels in a year. Arcturus was then thought to be about 40 light-years away, which means that the light which reaches your eyes as you look at the star tonight would have left it about 40 years ago! (See page 101.) In order to see how cumbersome the distance of Arcturus would be—expressed in miles—multiply the number of seconds in a year by 186,000 and then by 40. Or recall that light from the sun—93,000,000 miles away—comes to us in eight *minutes.*

Arcturus was chosen to "do the honors" at A Century of Progress because, since it was calculated to be about 40 light-years away, the beam which signaled the opening of the fair would have started from Arcturus at about the time that the Columbian Exposition, Chicago's previous "World's Fair," was going on in Jackson Park, in 1893.

Have you ever put a piece of paper under a lens or "magnifying glass" and let the rays of the sun focus on it? Soon a spot on the paper became hot, because the rays which would naturally fall on a larger area were focused on it. Perhaps the paper even caught fire. In the same way, the much fainter ray from Arcturus affected the photoelectric cell. So that clouds might not interfere, several telescopes were directed toward the star—at Harvard Observatory, Allegheny Observatory, the University of Illinois, and Yerkes Observatory—and it was arranged that these impulses be sent over telegraph lines to the Fair, where they opened the switches controlling the lighting.

To many people the nicest thing about Arcturus is that it is as sure a sign of coming spring as the first robin.

Fig. 12.—Boötes the Herdsman.

Though winter winds may still be blowing, when you first begin to see Arcturus at eight or nine o'clock in the evening, you know that springtime is not far away.

Arcturus is part of the constellation known as Boötes the Herdsman, or sometimes as Boötes the Bear Driver. Some versions of the legend of the Big Dipper say that Boötes is a hunter, the son of Callisto, who was placed in the sky just as he was without being changed into a bear. Not recognizing his mother in the Great Bear, Boötes pursues her in a constant chase around the polestar.

Some see the outline of a kite in the stars of Boötes,

23

and by comparing Figure 13 with Figure 14, you can see how well the two interpretations fit the same star group.

Near Boötes is Corona Borealis, the Northern Crown. It is a semicircle of stars, one of which is brighter than all the others. This star is called Alpha Coronae. Astronomers usually label individual stars of a group with the successive letters of the Greek alphabet, alpha (α), beta (β), gamma (γ), etc., approximately in the order of their brightness. Thus, the next brightest star in this constellation is Beta Coronae, the next Gamma Coronae, etc. The brightest star in Draco the Dragon is Alpha Draconis.

This use of Greek letters makes for greater standardiza-

FIG. 13.—The stars of Boötes as the Kite.

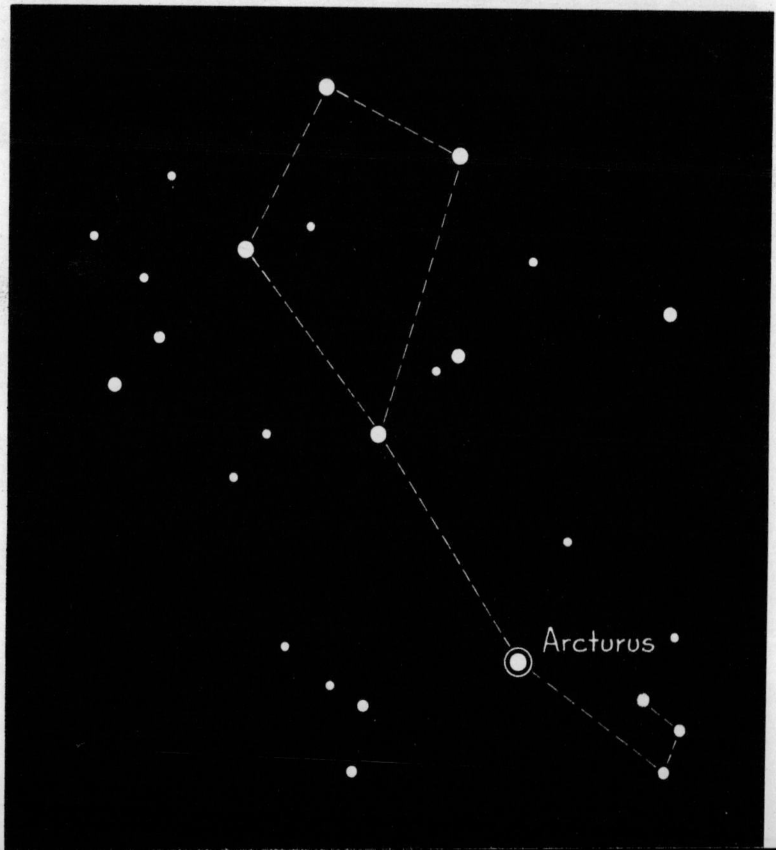

Fig. 14.—Corona and Boötes.

tion among names, so that astronomers all over the world know immediately which star is meant when it is mentioned. Also, it would not be practical to give individual names to all the 5,000 stars visible to the naked eye—not to mention the millions of telescopic stars—as we do to the more important stars, such as Arcturus, Polaris, Mizar, and Alcor.

However, in a few cases Greek letters are assigned to the stars of a constellation according to some other plan. In the case of the Big Dipper they follow the order of the stars, beginning with the Pointer nearest to Polaris, called Alpha Ursae Majoris, meaning Alpha of the Great Bear, and ending with the last star in the handle, called Eta Ursae Majoris.

There is a romantic legend to account for the presence of the Northern Crown in the sky. After Crete had de-

25

feated Athens, the Cretan king, Minos, demanded a dreadful tribute from the Athenians. Each year a group of their youths and maidens were sent to Crete to be sacrificed to the Minotaur. This was a dreadful monster who lived in the labyrinth, which was a cave with a series of intricately winding passages. When Theseus, son of the king of Athens, came of age, he resolved to put an end to the sacrifice by accompanying the next tribute ship himself and slaying the monster.

However, when he reached Crete, his plans seemed sure to fail, for although King Minos readily agreed to his meeting the beast first, he took away his sword and locked him up in a dungeon along with the other intended victims. Just as Theseus was convinced that all was lost, the door of his dungeon opened and in came Ariadne, the daughter of King Minos. She gave him a sharp sword and a ball of cord and told him to fasten one end of the cord to the entrance and let the ball unwind in his hands as he went in to find the Minotaur. In this way he would be able to find his way out after the battle. Theseus was, of course, very grateful and said that he would have his father repay her richly with gold and jewels. She would have none of that. However, when he suggested that she marry him and return with him to Athens, she readily agreed.

The next day, after a terrible battle in the cave from which no one before him had returned alive, Theseus killed the beast and, with the help of the cord, found his way back. Quickly he sped to the ship where Ariadne had secretly conveyed the Athenians. Swiftly they set sail out of the harbor, bound for Athens. They stopped at the island of Naxos in the hope of obtaining fresh water, and all the voyagers landed to explore.

Ariadne was weary and wandered apart from the others to rest a bit on the banks of a small stream. She soon fell asleep, and there Theseus found her. Meanwhile, his enthusiasm for their marriage had faded considerably, for as time passed his wife's share in his success had seemed to lessen, and he now wondered why his gratitude to her had ever been so great. Also he wondered what his countrymen would say when he returned with the daughter of the hated King Minos as a bride. The idea came to him of sneaking off and leaving her on the island. Quickly he summoned his companions and embarked, leaving poor Ariadne alone on the seemingly deserted isle. For days the poor maiden sat on the seashore, unmindful of wind or rain, unable to believe that Theseus would not return in his Athenian vessel.

It so happened that the island of Naxos was the best loved by Bacchus, the god of mirth and revelry. One day he was strolling along the shore with his ivy-crowned companions, who followed, dancing and singing. They suddenly came upon Ariadne sitting on the sand at the water's edge, where for days she had been looking mournfully out to sea. She was frightened at the appearance of so many strangers, but Bacchus soothed her fears and won her confidence so that she soon forgot the fickle Theseus and consented to become Bacchus' wife. There was a joyous wedding ceremony, and as a marriage gift Bacchus placed on her brow a crown of seven glittering stars.

Ariadne lived a long and happy life, and when she died Bacchus left the island. Before setting sail he took Ariadne's seven-starred crown and threw it into the sky where it forms the bright constellation known as Corona Borealis, or the Northern Crown.

You will remember that we found Arcturus by following the curve of the handle of the Big Dipper back to it. If we continue this curve back farther toward the horizon, we come to the first-magnitude star Spica, which is visible in the spring and summer months in the early evening, and is remarkable for its blue-white light.

Fig. 15.—Continue the curve of the handle of the Big Dipper through Arcturus and you come to Spica.

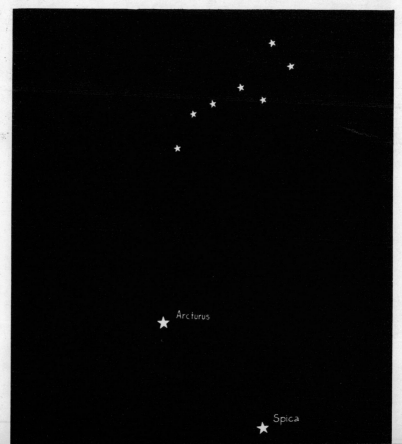

FIG. 16.—Constellation of the Virgin. (See Figure 41 also.)

Associated with Spica are stars forming the constellation of Virgo the Virgin. Spica is supposed to be in a sheaf of wheat in the Virgin's left hand. The word "spica" means "ear of wheat." The Virgin is a goddess of growth and plenty, and is supposed to be scattering grain to creatures on the earth.

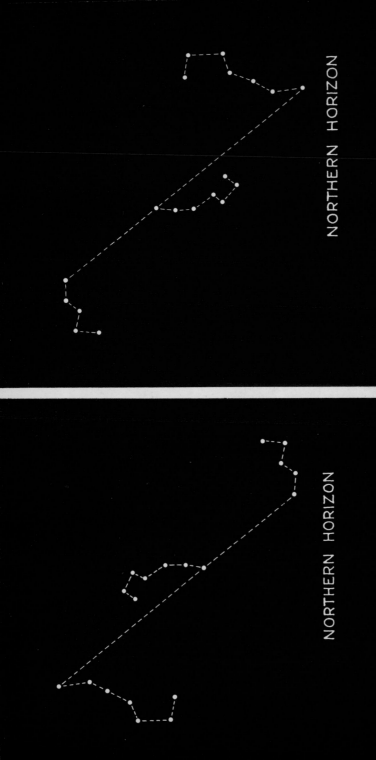

NORTHERN HORIZON

Fig. 18.—Relation of Cassiopeia
to the Dippers in winter.

NORTHERN HORIZON

Fig. 17.—Relation of Cassiopeia
to the Dippers in summer.

3. The Royal Family of the Sky

During our next stargazing evening, let us renew our acquaintance with the three circumpolars that we have met, and, if it is an early evening in spring or summer, pursue our friendship with Arcturus, Boötes, the Northern Crown, and Spica. For our next acquaintance, we shall meet some mutual friends of Arcturus and the Dipper. In doing this we shall be in good company, for we are about to meet the "royal family of the sky."

The first member of the family that we shall see resembles a giant, shallow W in the sky, or an M when its position is reversed. To find it, we must remember that it is always on the opposite side of Polaris from the Big Dipper. In the early evening in summer the W is usually near the horizon in the northeast, and in winter higher in the sky toward the northwest. It may not be in the same relation to the horizon as it is to the margin of the printed page, for its position in the sky, like that of the Big Dipper, varies with the hour and the season.

FIG. 19.—Cassiopeia forms a "W" in the sky.

FIG. 20.— There is a star just above the point of the "W."

This constellation is generally known as Cassiopeia, but is sometimes called Cassiopeia's Chair. One's first reaction to the name may be to question why it is not called Cassiopeia's W. The answer to this may be found if we look more closely at the star group. We now see a tiny extra star above the middle point of the W.

By changing a few of the imaginary lines between the stars and imagining one side as being on the ground, we can easily see a chair with a headrest.

There is a very interesting legend concerning Cassiopeia and the other members of the royal family of the sky. Cassiopeia, so the story goes, was queen of Ethiopia. She was very, very beautiful, but unfortunately she was well

FIG. 21.—With this star above the point of the "W" included, Cassiopeia's Chair is formed.

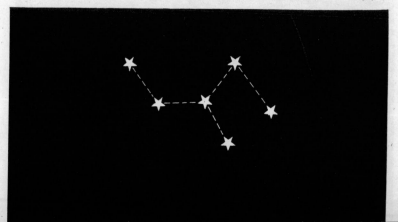

aware of it. Even more unfortunate was the fact that she could not refrain from talking of her beauty. In her vanity she boasted that she was even lovelier than the sea nymphs, who became angered and appealed to Neptune, god of the sea, to avenge the insult.

Neptune sent a dreadful monster to ravage the coast of the country where Cassiopeia was queen. Her husband, Cepheus the king, consulted the oracle of Jupiter, who informed him that the only way to make amends and turn away the evil that had come to his kingdom was to sacrifice his beautiful daughter, Andromeda, to the monster.

Compelled by his people to take this awful step to save them, Cepheus chained poor Andromeda to a rock along the shore. Crowds of people gathered along the water's edge, watching in horror as the monster approached. Nearer and nearer he came, and poor Andromeda's screams seemed of no avail. Struggle as she might, she could not loose herself from the chains. As in the modern thriller, we must leave our heroine helpless while we look into the doings of the hero. For, of course, there was a hero!

Perseus was a prince from another kingdom, a handsome, brave young man. The king of this country had sent Perseus in quest of the Gorgon Medusa, a horrible monster with snakes for hair who had recently terrorized the country. For whoever chanced to look at her turned immediately to stone. The country was fast becoming filled with stone monuments instead of living people!

Perseus set out after Medusa. He came to the abode

of the nymphs, who gave him winged sandals, a magic bag, and a helmet which made him invisible. He was fortunate enough to have the aid of the god Mercury and of Minerva, the goddess of wisdom. They cautioned him to polish his shield until he could see his face in it. When they approached the cave of the Gorgons, Minerva told Perseus not to look directly at Medusa.

"Look at the monster in your shield," the goddess advised him. "It is for this that you have kept it polished. And you must cut off her head with one blow, for you will not have a second chance."

Perseus flew down from the sky to the place where the Gorgon Medusa lay sleeping, and, looking in his shield, took careful aim and cut off her head. He stuffed it in his magic bag, and flew off. He breathed a sigh of thankfulness that the deed was done, for, to tell the truth, he had had his doubts that he would come out of the adventure alive!

At the time we meet Perseus he is flying through the air with his winged sandals, carefully holding the head of Medusa behind him. He was a brave young man, with the consciousness of a deed well done. He was anxious to get home. But his flight was suddenly interrupted by Andromeda's aforementioned screams. So, like a true movie hero, he arrived just in time to save her from the monster. Here was an adventure to his liking: a chance to rescue a beautiful princess!

Perseus swooped down toward Andromeda, holding the Medusa head in his magic bag. After calling to Andromeda not to look at him, he addressed the sea beast in a startling tone. He opened his bag, disclosing the head. The beast looked toward him, and fell in his tracks—turned to stone! Thus Perseus rescued the princess from her fate. They were married and lived happily ever after.

Legend says that the sea nymphs were angered when Cassiopeia was honored by being placed among the stars. So they prevailed upon Jupiter to place the queen's chair so that part of the night she was forced to hang head downward in the sky. Here we find Cassiopeia night after night, as she moves around the polestar following her husband, Cepheus the king. Some stargazers say that Cepheus is even more difficult to find than the Little Dipper, but let us try. We look for Cepheus, just ahead of Cassiopeia, as both of them move around Polaris. Cepheus looks like nothing so much as the five spot on a die, slightly slanted. Some observers include another star in the group, making a pentagon out of the figure.

Fig. 22.—Cassiopeia and Cepheus.

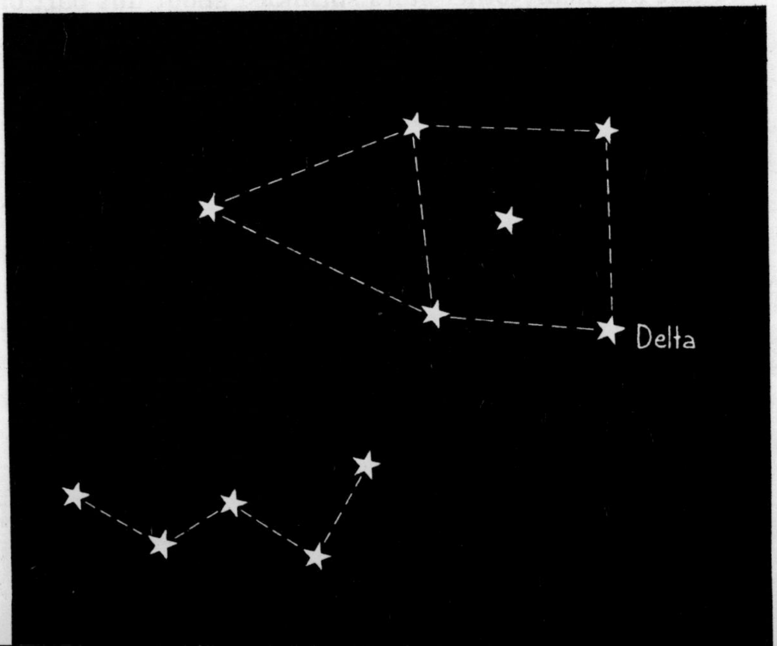

FIG. 23.—Cepheus the King.

There are many other stars sprinkled about this part of the sky, and the principal stars are faint, which adds to our difficulty. As before, the best way to see the constellation is to be sure to have a clear idea of what you are looking for, and then all of a sudden it will seem to pop out at you from the surrounding stars. The best way to make Cepheus look like a man is to imagine him in a costume as shown in Figure 23, with arms outstretched and with a sword in his belt, using only the five stars making up the four-sided figure.

In the sky south[1] of Cassiopeia on autumn and early

[1] "North" from any star in the sky is the direction along the line joining it with the polestar; "south" is the opposite direction.

Fig. 24.—The Royal Family. Early evening view in eastern sky in summer; later on in the year the constellation will have swung farther along to the west at the same hour.

37

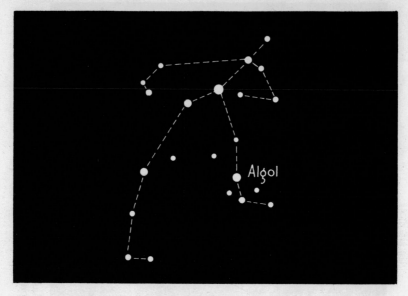

FIG. 25.—Perseus.

winter evenings are Perseus and Andromeda, and Pegasus, the flying horse.

Perseus is a beautiful constellation, tall and long-legged. He is holding the head of Medusa behind him—fortunately for us, lest it turn us to stone!

Perhaps the easiest way to locate Andromeda is to first find the Square of Pegasus. Its sides vary in length from about 13 degrees to nearly 18 degrees, and the four stars which make it up are bright enough to make it easy to pick out in the sky. The "square" forms the body of the horse; his neck stretches out toward the southwest and his forefeet to the northwest. According to most legends Pegasus sprang from the fallen body of the Gorgon after she was slain by Perseus, and after an exciting career of flying about between earth and sky,

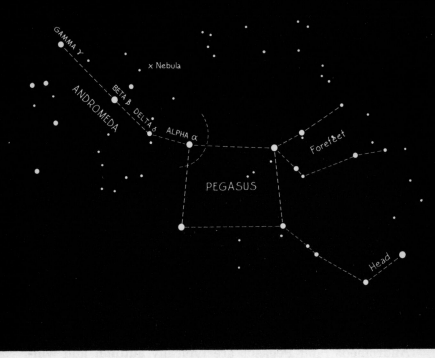

FIG. 26.—Andromeda and Pegasus.

the winged horse was finally placed among the stars. However, you can think of Pegasus as tied to Andromeda's rock.

The constellation of Andromeda is outlined by a row of four bright stars beginning in the northeast corner of the Square of Pegasus. In fact, Alpha Andromedae is part of the Square. As can be seen in Figure 26, the principal stars of Andromeda and Pegasus look like an immense dipper, with the handle running northeast across the heavens for 30 degrees in a slightly curved and easily traced line under Cassiopeia. This line of stars represents Andromeda chained to the rock. Alpha marks her head, Delta her shoulder—from which an arm is outstretched

—and Gamma her foot. They are all second-magnitude stars except Delta, which is of the third magnitude. As seen through most telescopes, Gamma will appear to us as a double star—made up of an orange star and a blue star.

The family portrait in Figure 24 will give you an idea of the appearance and locations of Cassiopeia, Cepheus, Andromeda, Perseus, and Pegasus. As Cassiopeia makes its daily circle around the polestar, they turn also— sometimes seeming to be climbing up the sky in the east, and sometimes to be climbing down in the west. In the northern half of the United States, the two older folks, Cassiopeia and Cepheus, are circumpolar constellations. You will remember that this means they are visible at any hour of the night no matter what the date. Perseus, Andromeda, and Pegasus are typically autumn and winter constellations. Of course, we may see them in summer, but not so early in the night as in the fall and winter months. Just after it becomes dark in late January, Cassiopeia may be seen directly above the polestar; soon after dark six months later, it may be seen directly below the polestar.

The members of the royal family always appear so bright and sparkling that they seem to be enjoying a reunion in the sky, Cassiopeia long since cured of her vanity. They appear much too jolly to serve as a warning against conceit. At any rate, it is thrilling to know that in the dim past men looked at these same stars with enough interest to concoct this 4,000-year-old legend about the star group.

VARIABLE STARS AND NOVAE

The modern scientist, as well as the fanciful stargazer, regards this group of constellations with great interest. In Figures 24 and 25, the star which is near the bottom of the hero's left leg is Algol. This star is in Medusa's head, which Perseus holds by the hair in his left hand. It is a variable star, losing two-thirds of its brightness at intervals of about three days. The diminishing process takes about five hours; the star remains dim for about twenty minutes; then its former brightness is recovered again in about five hours. This phenomenon is caused by the presence of a large, faint companion star, whose diameter is a little greater than that of Algol. These two stars revolve around each other so close together that they appear as a single star; the fainter companion partially obscures Algol's light when it is between Algol and the earth. The loss in light when Algol is between its companion and the earth is barely noticeable.

Many stars are not constant in brightness. Polaris, the North Star, shows a regular fluctuation extending over a longer period of time than that of Algol. Several of the stars in Cepheus are notably variable, especially Delta. The type of star which it represents is called a "Cepheid variable." Such changes in brightness are probably due to alternate expansion and contraction of the star, which beats like a giant heart. The cause of this pulsation has not been determined, but astronomers have discovered that the lengths of the periods of expansion and contraction are dependent on the star's true brightness. By comparison of this true brightness with the apparent bright-

41

ness of the star, as we see it, the distances of a great many stars have been determined.

Novae are stars which burst suddenly into great splendor and then dwindle until they become invisible except with the aid of powerful telescopes. The word *nova* means "new," but the stars to which the term is applied are not new. Though usually quite faint, such a star is almost always recorded very faintly on earlier photographs at the location in the sky where it later flashes out with a brilliance which is sometimes thousands of times greater than that which it possessed even one or two days before.

The first brilliant nova ever recorded appeared near the end of 1572 in the constellation of Cassiopeia. It is usually known as Tycho's star, because a great many observations of it were made by the great astronomer, Tycho Brahe. When he first noticed this star, it belonged to the first magnitude. In less than a month it grew so bright as to cause comment all over the civilized world and could be seen in broad daylight. In about six months this supernova had apparently vanished completely, although it could have been seen with moderately large telescopes.

Near the end of February, 1901, a nova was discovered in Perseus after it had already become a star of the first magnitude. Photographs of the constellation taken three nights earlier showed this star as very faint. In less than three days it had increased over 100,000 times in brightness. Soon after its discovery it became the third brightest star in the heavens. Twenty-four hours later it had lost one third of its brightness, and within a year had faded so that it was visible only through a telescope.

The sudden brightness of novae is probably caused by a shell of very hot gas blown out from the star at the time of increased brightness. But why stars "blow up" in this way is still a mystery.

Variable stars and novae are not so rare as might be expected. You can notice the variability of Algol with the naked eye. It is not at all improbable that some novae will be discovered in the years while you are stargazing. Though the majority of these will be visible only through a telescope, perhaps some will be brilliant enough for you to see. You may even become so familiar with the heavens that you will detect the presence of a nova before it is announced in the newspapers!

OTHER UNIVERSES THAN OURS

The royal family, then, is quite distinguished: Perseus has Algol, Cepheus its variables, and Cassiopeia its supernova. But it is the Great Nebula in Andromeda that claims the greatest attention of modern scientists and inspires the awe of staregazers. To use a homely simile, observing this nebula has much the same fascination as looking through a knothole at a baseball game to which we do not have the price of admission. The Andromeda Nebula is so vast that although it is nearly a million light-years distant we can see it in a clear, dark sky with the naked eye as a faint, fuzzy patch of light. For its position in Andromeda, see Figure 24 or Figure 26.

In a photograph it is a thing of marvelous beauty, appearing like a great wheel with a hub in the center (see

Fig. 27.—Great Spiral Nebula in Andromeda. This galaxy is 800,000 light-years distant—the most distant object visible to the naked eye.

Figure 27). Historically, it is important because it was the first nebula to become known. In the latter part of the eighteenth century, Sir William Herschel, with telescopes of his own making, spent his nights surveying one after another of the various objects in the sky. Among his many discoveries none mystified him more than nebulae, the irregular patches of faint light scattered here and there among the stars. As he made larger and larger telescopes, he found that many of the nebulae appeared to break up into clusters of stars. Others, like the Great Nebula in Andromeda defied even his strongest lenses. What were they?

Also, as Herschel looked at the sky, he was impressed by the great number of faint stars forming the Milky Way. Almost everyone has observed that great band extending diagonally across the sky, passing through Cassiopeia and Cepheus. This band extends all the way around the sky, although only about half of it is visible at any one time. Within it faint stars are so thickly set as to give the appearance of a stream of milk spilled on the dark blue floor of the sky. Dante said of it, "Pricked out with less and greater lights, . . . the Milky Way so gleameth white as to set very sages questioning." Astronomers believe that there are at least 100 billions of stars in this portion of the jeweled sky. It was Herschel's belief that all the stars were roughly of the same brightness, so that he was seeing many *distant* stars when he looked at the Milky Way. He therefore reasoned that our universe must extend to a greater distance along the circular band formed by the Milky Way.

Approximate location
of Sun and Planets

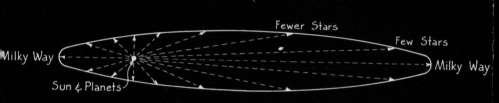

Fewer Stars

Few Stars

Milky Way

Milky Way

Sun & Planets

Fig. 28.—A diagram of the supposed shape of our galaxy, in cross-section, showing why our sky has a Milky Way.

Thus he gave us a picture of our universe—or, as it is called, our galaxy—in the shape of a grindstone. In his picture our sun is one of a million or more stars somewhere near the center of this "grindstone." Our earth is too close to the sun to be shown as a separate dot on the diagram. From the earth we look out into the universe and see stars in all directions. The stars appear most numerous when we look out toward the rim of the grindstone-shaped galaxy (see Figure 28)—the bright band called the Milky Way. At right angles to it, we are looking along its thin dimension. Hence we see fewer stars.

It is truly remarkable that the twentieth-century picture of our galaxy differs little from that first imagined by Herschel, except that it is much larger and the sun is now known to be off-center. This was shown by Dr. Harlow

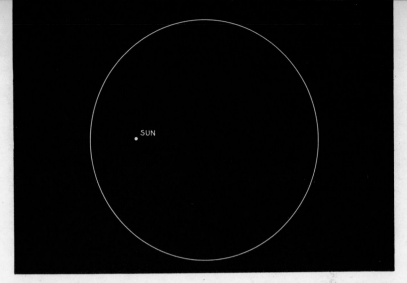

F<small>IG</small>. 29.—Diagrammatic view of our galaxy at right angles to Fig. 28, showing approximate position of our sun.

Shapley of Harvard Observatory, who located the galaxy center from a study of faint star clusters grouped in a large sphere around a point 30,000 light-years away from us.

But what has all this to do with the Andromeda Nebula? Herschel went even further than his picture of our own galaxy. He believed that many of the disk-shaped patches of light in the sky similar to the Andromeda Nebula are other galaxies, independent and remote from ours. He called them "island universes." Modern astronomers, using large telescopes capable of photographing very faint stars, have verified this by photographs showing the individual stars of the Andromeda Nebula and others. Recent work with the largest telescopes shows that there are at least 100 million of these other galaxies out as far as can be seen. These "island universes" are so remote from one another that it takes light millions of years to cross the intervening space. Each of these galaxies is made up of billions of suns, and each sun has the possibility of

47

being the center of a solar system like that of our own.

Thus have the frontiers of space been pushed farther and farther from our own little planet. Men first believed that our own earth was the center of the universe: its beginning and its end; that the sun moved from east to west in the sky for our particular benefit; that the stars were heavenly streetlights, so to speak. Centuries later, astronomers showed us that we were part of a solar system: that our earth, along with her eight sister planets, moves around the sun. Then we learned that even this sun is not the center of the universe; each star in the sky is a sun. Telescopes revealed that there are about 100 billion of them, grouped in a wheel-shaped galaxy so vast that light, traveling at the incredible speed of 186,000 miles a second takes 100,000 years to cross from one side of

Fig. 30.—Hypothetical cross-section of space, showing island universes or galaxies.

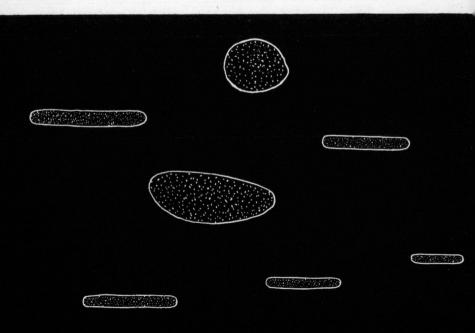

it to the other—and our sun is far from the central position in this galaxy. Beyond the limits of our galaxy there are many other galaxies scattered throughout space as far as can be seen. The largest of these others so far known to us is that one which we see as the Andromeda Nebula; it takes light 80,000 years to cross it, or four-fifths of the time it takes to cross our galaxy. Remote indeed are the boundaries of the universe! Such vast distances and huge numbers are beyond our comprehension.

We can illustrate our insignificant position in space by suggesting what might be our "complete address." Were spatial communication within the realm of possibility, mailing directions such as this would be necessary:

Miss Mary Smith
  1011 Linden Avenue
    Chicago, Illinois
      U. S. A.
        Planet Earth, Solar System of the Sun
          Island Universe or Galaxy #290 (Let us say)
            Near Andromeda Galaxy
            Space

The celestial mail sorter would note that the letter was directed to someone living on Earth, a planet of the Sun —a star in a galaxy called Island Universe #290 (we pretend). This is one of many galaxies somewhere near the Andromeda Galaxy. Once on earth it is a simple matter to deliver it to Miss Mary Smith. If the mailman traveled with the speed of light, the letter might be delivered many millions of years after it had been posted from another galaxy! The whole impossible procedure suggests the remoteness and minuteness of our earth in space.

4. Summer Triangle and Company

Now we have become familiar with three groups of constellations: The Big Dipper group, the Arcturus group, and the royal family. At this point it gives one quite a triumphant feeling to go out some evening and be able to recognize these new friends—nine of them—in the sky. Do not rush matters. Be sure that you become really well acquainted with each one, and that you think of the interesting and wonderful things that each suggests. Then, one evening, you will feel that it is time to broaden your acquaintance. If it is summertime, perhaps you would be interested in making the acquaintance of the Summer Triangle and its associated star groups.

The Summer Triangle is distinguished by the fact that it is formed by three stars of the first magnitude, Vega, Altair, and Deneb. It is best to make one's first search for it on a summer evening, for the triangle is most conspicuous then. Later in the year or night its position in the sky makes it hard to see. If you equip yourself with sky maps, you should be able to find the triangle even then. The best way to become familiar with it is to keep looking, winter, summer, spring, and fall, until you know its varying positions. Or a single evening spent in watching the stars off and on from darkness to midnight will teach you more about the apparent movement of the sky than you could learn from a dozen books.

FIG. 31.—The Summer Triangle.

If it is summertime, look over in the east, slightly north, and you cannot fail to see three extraordinarily bright stars in the shape of a triangle. The longer sides of this triangle are 30 degrees or so in length. The fact that the Milky Way passes through the Summer Triangle may help you locate it. Also, when Arcturus is in the sky, it is more than 60 degrees southwest of Vega. When you look for the Summer Triangle do not underestimate its size.

Vega is truly "Queen of the Summer Sky." Besides being a very noticeable bluish-white star, it is also the brightest star in the summer sky and second brightest of the stars visible at 40 degrees north latitude. On summer evenings Arcturus is its nearest rival. If you watch the sky when it is just beginning to get dark, you will see that Vega and Arcturus are the first stars to appear.[1] How many, many people have made wishes to them to the tune of "Star light, star bright, first star I see tonight. . . . !"

When we were looking at the Big Dipper, we learned that the suns which appear to us as the stars of that constellation are moving independently at such speeds that in 100,000 years they will no longer form the outline of a dipper in the sky. Our sun, also a star, has a motion of its own. Taking all its planets, including the earth, with it, it is moving in the direction of Vega at the rate of 400 million miles a year. The distance of Vega from us is so enormous, however, that no appreciable change in its brightness will be noticeable in the next 10,000 years.

Each of the three stars in the Summer Triangle, Vega, Deneb, and Altair, has a constellation as its escort. Vega is part of a constellation called the Lyre. Altair is in

[1] Excepting the planets, which are described in Chapter 8.

FIG. 32.—Two representations of Vega and the Lyre.

FIG. 33.—Aquila the Eagle, in its simplest form.

Aquila the Eagle, which looks very much like an airplane. Deneb is one of the stars in Cygnus the Swan, also called the Northern Cross. When we view all three constellations together we see quite an imposing group of stars, one that the Greeks could hardly have failed to notice and weave tales about.

Apollo, the Greek god of music, once gave a lyre to Orpheus, the son of Calliope and Apollo. Since the lyre had been the gift of Apollo and was played by one with as much skill and love of music as Orpheus, the melodies were like none ever heard on earth before. When he played, rivers ceased in their courses, the birds hushed their songs, and the very rocks pricked up their ears to listen to the magical music that came from his lyre.

Orpheus fell in love with a beautiful girl named Eurydice. On their wedding day, they were walking through a field when a venomous serpent bit Eurydice's heel, and she died.

Alas, no tears of Orpheus nor music of his lyre could bring her back. Orpheus was desolate. He played his lyre no more, but wandered alone, distracted by grief. He begged Apollo to give Eurydice back to him. Apollo said

53

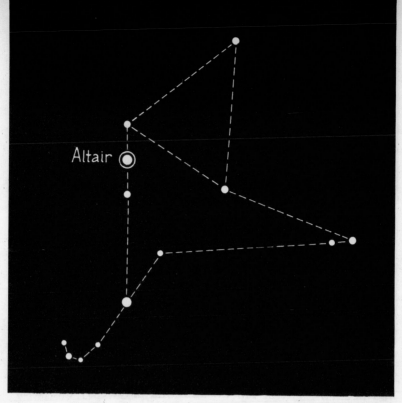

Altair

FIG. 34.—Entire constellation of Aquila the Eagle.

that he was powerless to do this, but that he would give
Orpheus an entrance to the underworld so that he might
entreat Pluto, king of the dark realm, to give him back
his bride.

Orpheus entered the gate of the dread underworld,
made his way past Cerberus, the three-headed dog, past
the serpents, past the other guardians, charming them all
with his beautiful music.

At last he stood before Pluto's throne. He made his plea
and played upon his lyre. "Iron tears" rolled down Pluto's
cheeks, and he granted Orpheus' request. He made one
condition: Orpheus was to start out alone. Eurydice was

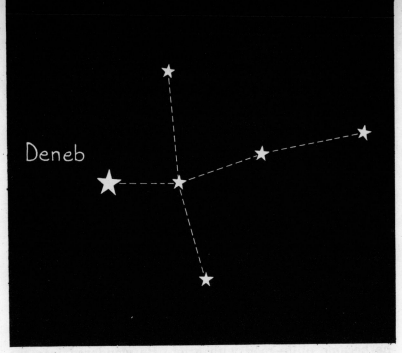

FIG. 35.—Deneb and the Northern Cross.

FIG. 36.—Cygnus the Swan.

to follow a few paces back. He must not so much as glance at her until he had passed the entrance to the upper world. Orpheus started out, playing his lyre. Soon doubts began to assail him. Had Eurydice really started? Was Pluto cheating him? Finally, he could stand it no longer. He looked around. Eurydice was there, even more beautiful than in earthly life. She called faintly to him and then vanished before his eyes in a cloud of mist.

Orpheus stood aghast, unable to realize what had happened. Finally, the fact that Eurydice was gone became clear to him, and sadly he made his way into the upper world. The charm was broken. He could no longer make his way back through Pluto's realms.

Orpheus mourned so much for his lost Eurydice that he became quite mad with grief. He wandered into the mountains and came to a violent end at the hands of some wild followers of Bacchus. At his death Apollo asked Jupiter to place Orpheus' magical lyre among the stars, and it became the constellation Lyra.

Some legends state that Orpheus himself was transformed into a swan, and as the constellation of Cygnus placed near Lyra, his beloved lyre.

At the opposite end of the Lyre from Vega a small telescope will show the Ring Nebula—a faint glowing doughnut in the sky. Although the ancient Greeks never saw it, they might easily have introduced this remarkable object into their legends as the ring on the finger of the lyre player! The Ring Nebula is very different from the Andromeda Nebula, although its fuzzy appearance earned it a similar name. Studies of its light show that it is a glowing cloud of gas composed mostly of hydrogen, helium, oxygen, and nitrogen. Perhaps the most peculiar fact is that there are over one hundred other such nebulae in the sky, and that at the center of each a faint star gleams. Astronomers believe that these small central stars may have suffered violent explosions long ago, and blew off shells of hot gas, each of which continues to glow in the light from its parent star.

These spheres of gas are hundreds of times larger than the distance from sun to earth, but much smaller and closer to us than the Andromeda Nebula. We shall see other forms of gaseous nebulae in other constellations, most of them near the Milky Way, a result of the fact that they are in our galaxy.

Cygnus the Swan is also sometimes called the Northern Cross. At Christmas time around 10 P.M. nightly this constellation can be seen standing on the northwestern horizon like a starry cross set up above the earth. Deneb is the bright first-magnitude star at the top of the cross.

Radiobroadcasting has recently brought scientific fame to Cygnus, the Northern Cross. It is not the kind of broadcast you would want to listen to, nor can you pick it up on an ordinary radio. During the war years, short-wave sets of the type used for radar were found to pick up more "static" (irregular noise) when the Milky Way was overhead than when it was not. Special aerials like large dishes were soon built to find from what direction these noisy radio waves were coming, and a "broadcasting" region was found in Cygnus. Although the sun (and presumably all similar stars) are also found to "broadcast," the remarkable fact is that no star has yet been found in the direction of the Cygnus "radio station." Apparently in some dark region of space nature's own conditions are right for broadcasting radio signals billions of times stronger than those of the largest man-made radio station. It is disappointing that these gusts of electrified gas between the stars broadcast only harsh noises, a far cry from the harmonious "music of the spheres" which men have expected from the stars since Thomas Browne wrote of it in 1663.

A sight of the Northern Cross brings to mind the celebrated Southern Cross, so far away yet also set in the softly glowing Milky Way. Although the Northern Cross forms a more perfect cross than its counterpart of the Southern Hemisphere, it has never fired our imagination to the same degree. This is partly because the southern starry cross, the "Four Stars" of Amerigo Vespucci, was first brought to the attention of the modern world by the explorers and adventurers of the late Middle Ages and so is a part of the heritage of those years which saw the New World opened. Partly it is because, as a symbol of those lands of our "Good Neighbors" to the south, it has always beckoned to us with the lure of friendly yet unfamiliar charm. For the Southern Cross belongs to the South Americans and Australians as surely as the Big Dipper belongs to us. Although it can be seen from southern Florida and parts of Texas, when viewed from there it is so near the horizon that the brightness of its stars does not show to full advantage.

Should you travel south, it would be well to look over maps of the sky as viewed from the Southern Hemisphere and learn about the constellations visible there. Even on such a trip some of the friends you are now making among the stars will stay with you, for many which you see here are shared with the Southern Hemisphere.

South of Deneb and east of Altair a small diamond-shaped constellation made up of tiny stars twinkles so that it reminds one of an electric sign in the distance. This is Job's Coffin, or Delphinus the Dolphin. It is one of the few constellations named for a Biblical character. The faithful Job, you remember, was too good a man to be buried in the earth, and so, it is said, Jehovah decreed that he was to be buried halfway between heaven and

Fig. 37.—The Summer Triangle and Company as they appear in the eastern sky on a summer evening. Vega is nearly overhead.

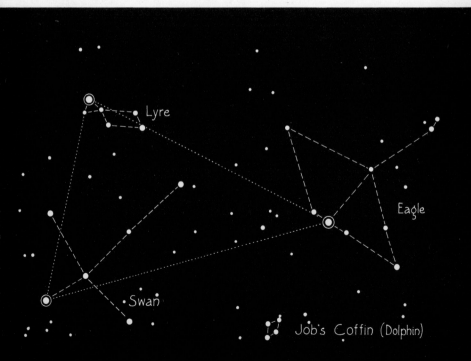

Lyre

Eagle

Swan

Job's Coffin (Dolphin)

earth. The Hebrew shepherds in later ages, watching their flocks on the hills of Palestine, connected this box-like group of stars with the coffin of the immortal Job.

Now we can see the Summer Triangle in its entirety. Mostly characteristic of the happy days of summer, it is with us almost every night of the year. In winter or in the early morning hours of a summer day, its changed position makes it appear quite different. Can you find Vega, Deneb, and Altair? Associated with Vega do you see the Lyre? Near it can you see Deneb in the Northern Cross, farther from it Altair in the Eagle? Near Altair little Job's Coffin twinkles brightly. These are five new friends.

5. More "Stars of the Summer Night"

Each night when you have gone out to meet new star friends, you have probably renewed your acquaintance with the ones we learned about earlier. It is a good plan. Renewed acquaintance with the stars adds greatly to our appreciation of them. We cannot expect to learn everything in one session.

The Summer Triangle and Company were easy to find, so shall we tackle something a bit more difficult now? If it is summertime, let us try to find Hercules, a constellation whose name suggests its mythical origin. Hercules, in ancient mythology, was the great grandson of the hero Perseus. Hercules himself had the reputation of being the greatest of earthly heroes, having performed seemingly impossible tasks and tremendous feats of strength.

Strangely enough, this star group is also called "The

FIG. 38.—Hercules in relation to Vega and Arcturus.

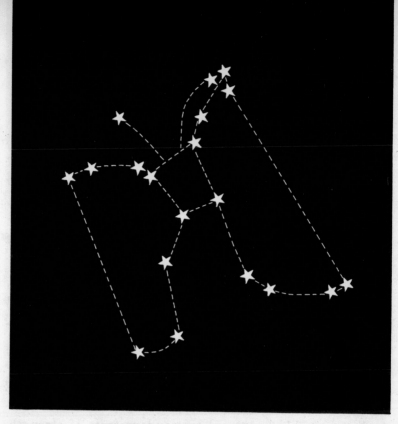

Fig. 39.—Hercules as the Butterfly.

Butterfly," a creature which the arrangement of the stars does suggest. Hercules fills the space between Arcturus and Vega. (Do you remember how to find them?) On summer evenings it is near the zenith, the point directly overhead. When you are using Figure 38, imagine it suspended over your head; remember to look for Hercules with the Lyre east of the zenith and the Kite to the west. First look for the "wastebasket" which forms the body, about halfway on the line between Vega and the Crown, then trace out the arms and legs.

The main point of interest in Hercules is its celebrated

Fig. 40.—Great Globular Star Cluster in Hercules.

globular star cluster, which, seen through an opera glass, appears as a faint and fuzzy disk. While looking at the Andromeda Nebula, we learned that Herschel, with larger telescopes, found many of the fuzzy patches he called nebulae are tight star clusters in our own galaxy. About a hundred more have been found, all nearly of the same form. These are the clusters which Shapley studied to locate the center of our galaxy.

Fig. 41.—Relation of Berenice's Hair to Spica and Arcturus.

Study of photographs of the Hercules cluster shows it made up of about 40 or 50 thousand stars, making the average distance between these stars about one light-year. Thus, as Garrett P. Serviss[1] says, if a planet were moving around a star near the center of the cluster, the dwellers on that planet "would enjoy the spectacle of a starry firmament incomparably more splendid than that which we behold." While we see only about 2,000 stars on a clear night, of which but a few are conspicuous and about two-thirds so faint that they are hard to distinguish, a spectator at the center of the Hercules cluster would behold many thousands of stars at once, most of them brighter than any we see. Indeed, four or five of the brightest ones would give more light than does our full moon. The stars of the outside universe, the ones which we know, would be inconspicuous among the numerous closer stars of the cluster. Such an observer would be largely closed up within his own star system, knowing little of the universe beyond the brilliant cluster which to us is but a faint patch of light, unnoticed except when our attention is called to it.

If it is spring or summer, just north of Spica and to the right of Arcturus will be seen a group of glimmering stars. Their curious twinkling light will catch your eye. This is the constellation of Berenice's Hair. Look at it with the aid of field or opera glasses, and you will then be able to see twenty or thirty of the brightest stars composing this large loose cluster—which is truly a lovely sight.

The constellation has a very romantic history. It is re-

[1] Serviss, Garrett P., *Astronomy with an Opera Glass* (D. Appleton-Century), p. 45.

lated that Queen Berenice, whose young husband went to war, vowed that she would sacrifice her beautiful hair to Venus if he might be allowed to return victorious over his enemies. He did return home in triumph, and Berenice, true to her vow, cut off her tresses and laid them on the altar of Venus. But that same night they disappeared. Poor Berenice wept bitterly at the loss, and her husband was most angry. He threatened to do all sorts of things to the guardians of the temple to punish them for their carelessness. But a celebrated astronomer named Conon came to the rescue. That evening he showed the young king and queen the missing locks, shining transfigured and beautiful in the sky. He assured them that Venus had been so pleased with the offering that she had put them there. As they were not stargazers, they were quite ready to believe that the silvery swarm of stars near Arcturus had never been there before. It rather pleased them to believe it, too! The legend goes that ever since that time the constellation has been known as Berenice's Hair.

Just west of Berenice's Hair, shining almost overhead in the evening if it is springtime, is Leo the Lion. Later in the summer he is nearer the western horizon and seems to be stalking along the land. Look first for the sickle which forms the forepart of the lion, with a bright star in the end of its handle. This star group appeared in the legends of many ancient peoples, always as a lion; to the Hebrews as the Lion of Judah, to the Greeks as the Nemean Lion, put there to commemorate Hercules' victory over him. Regulus, a first-magnitude star, is the heart of the lion.

FIG. 42.—Leo the Lion in relation to Berenice's Hair and the Manger.

Near the third star in the sickle, starting with Regulus, is a very faint companion star, making a pair similar to Mizar and Alcor in the Big Dipper.

Leo is one of the constellations of the zodiac, as shown in Figure 43. The circle around the center of the figure represents the earth's path around the sun, with the stars in the vast distance represented by the outer circle. When the earth is at A, we see the sun in the line A-Z as if it were among the stars at Z. And we say that the sun is entering the constellation Leo. Actually, the stars of Leo are many light-years farther away from us than the sun and form a background for it, which is usually obscured by the bright sky in the daytime. But just after sunset we are able to see the stars that are near the sun. Thus when the sun is entering Leo, we would see Leo low in the west just after sunset.

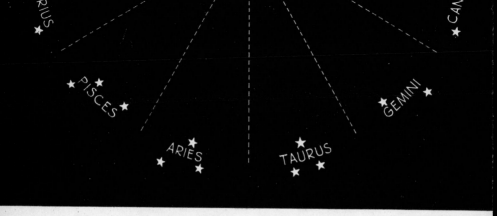

FIG. 43.—Constellations of the zodiac. Inner circle is the orbit of the earth, with *A* and *B* successive positions of the earth.

As we are being carried on the earth from *A* to *B*, the sun seems to be moving from Z to Y. When the sun seems to be among the stars at Y, it appears to enter the constellation Virgo; Virgo would then be on the western horizon just after sunset. And so on through the year until the earth has made a complete trip around the sun and is back at *A*.

The ancients gave the name *ecliptic* to this imaginary line from constellation to constellation which the sun appeared to follow around the sky on its annual course. They saw also that the moon and five other moving "stars," which they called planets or "wanderers," followed nearly the same general course as the sun among the stars, moving in a belt extending about 8 degrees on each side of the ecliptic. They named this belt the *zodiac*, and divided it into twelve equal parts, each about 30 degrees long, and marked by twelve constellations, the sun passing through one of them in the course of each month. Thus arose the familiar signs of the zodiac, stock-in-trade of the astrologers and horoscope writers.

Since this motion is so regular, you can find the constellation in which the sun is located on any date in the year in the following way: Start with August 10 as the day the sun enters the constellation Leo; on September 10 it enters Virgo; on October 10, Libra; etc.[2]

In this book we shall not attempt to discuss all the constellations which are signs of the zodiac, for many of them are difficult to see. However, by the time you finish the book you should be able to find eight of the twelve.

Look now about 15 degrees to the west of the sickle of Leo. If it is a clear night, your eye will be attracted by a silvery spot in the sky lying between two faint stars. This is the star group which is known to some as the Manger (see Figure 42), and it is in the constellation of Cancer

[2]The astrologers, for elaborate reasons, prefer to reckon the changes of the signs on the 22d of each month.

the Crab, one of the constellations of the zodiac. The two stars which are located on each side of the Manger were known to the ancients as the "ass's colts," and they were pictured as eating from the manger. With a small hand telescope you can see that the Manger consists of a crowd of stars so small that you cannot possibly count them. Sometimes it is called the Beehive, because through the telescope the nest of stars looks like a swarm of golden bees. It is a star cluster, not of the globular sort, and not so large nor so far away as the one in Hercules. Its interesting feature is the fact that the ancients used it as a weather sign. When the Manger could be seen, they believed that fair weather lay ahead, but when it was obscured by misty atmosphere a storm was on its way. This has long been known as a true weather proverb.

6. Look to the South

If it is summertime or early autumn let us study the southern sky, for a group of constellations there will merit our attention. The first one we shall meet is Scorpius the Scorpion. Few constellations bear so close a resemblance to the objects for which they are named as this one.

Scorpius can always be recognized by its fiery, first-magnitude star, Antares, whose light-giving power is many hundred times as great as that of our sun. Antares is the heart of the great scorpion which, according to legend, frightened the horses of the sun so that the driver lost control of them, and in their headlong flight the sun

FIG. 44.—Scorpius the Scorpion.

chariot almost collided with the earth. The fiery sun came so close to the surface of the earth that it scorched a wide area in Africa that has since become known as the Sahara Desert, so the legend goes. This monster is also said to have killed Orion with its poisonous sting. It is interesting in this connection to note that the two constellations Orion and Scorpius are never visible at the same time.

The rosy color of Antares, chief sparkler of Scorpius, is very remarkable. So much so that perhaps it will set us thinking of the range of colors that the stars have thus far presented to us: orange-colored Arcturus, white Altair, blue-white Vega. Astronomers have discovered that star colors are very closely related to star temperatures. Fiery Antares is a fairly cool star, only red-hot; its temperature is around 3,000 degrees. Orange-colored Arcturus is a little warmer; yellow Capella, which you will meet later, is about twice as hot as Arcturus; and yellow-white Procyon, which you will also meet later, is hotter than Capella. And we have white-hot stars like Altair and blue-hot ones like Spica, the latter having a temperature of around 20,000 degrees.

While we are discovering why one star is red and another yellow, we may wonder also why some are faint and some are bright. Of course, the distance of the star from us is one of the factors which determine this. But even if all the stars were the same distance from us they would not all be equally bright; in other words, they differ in intrinsic brightness. This is due partly to difference in temperature and partly to difference in size. Large stars which are less hot may give as much heat and light as small, hot ones.

Why are there different types of stars? Astronomers tell us that stars are in different stages of growth and that the youth, middle age, and elderly years of the stars may be read in their size and color. Of course, we have never seen a star grow. We observers are in a similar position to an inhabitant of another globe dropped in an earthly forest for the first time and able to stay there only for a few minutes. He might find acorns, oak leaves, oak saplings, and mighty oak trees. He would not be there long enough to see anything actually grow. But from the presence of these various stages in the life history of an oak, he might be able to describe the changes in the life of the tree from acorn to rotting log.

By like methods astronomers picture the life history of a star. The matter is as yet speculative; its proof or disproof awaits knowledge not yet ours and observations not yet made. They tell us that all stars came from the condensation of masses of gas. There is no proof of this, for when we wish to study the stages of growth which are actually present, we start with the newborn star, with the ball of gas sufficiently condensed that we may really call it a star. Newborn stars are very large bodies hardly red-hot. Antares belongs to this class. Arcturus is a bit older. As discussed in a later section, page 160, it is now believed that stars radiate heat and light at the expense of some of the material of which they are made. Shining gradually lessens their weight and size, and, as time goes on and more heat is given out, the star becomes smaller and hotter. It reaches white heat or blue heat by liberation of energy and then seems to be at a turning point in its career. It begins to cool, so that in time the star again becomes red, but smaller than it was originally. The star begins to fade in brilliance, having started on the downhill grade, headed toward extinction.

Astronomers tell us that our sun is about halfway between its period of maximum and its period of extinction. We can see our sun's past as it became hotter in the line of red-hot, yellow-hot, white-hot, and blue-hot stars, and we can foresee its future as it becomes cooler in a long line of stars, fainter and fainter, down to small red-hot ones about the size of our sun's largest planet. Just before the end of their career, after shrinking and cooling more and more, many stars seem to make a mighty effort to postpone their end as long as possible. Their surfaces again become white-hot, due to the activity of what Dr. Menzel of Harvard Observatory[1] calls "second childhood." He tells us that some of these white-hot stars, dwarfs, as they are called, are as small as the earth. Since they were once as large as Antares, which, if placed in the position of our sun, would reach out beyond the orbit of Mars, they are now so compressed that they are made of very heavy material. There is a star near Sirius, a star we shall meet later, that is made of material weighing almost 2,000 pounds per teaspoonful! It seems almost unbelievable that anything could be so dense.

These white dwarfs are very faint; unless they are near our sun we cannot see them even through the strongest

[1] Menzel, Donald H., *Stars and Planets* (The University Society, Inc.), p. 96.

74

telescope. There are probably many of these stars of which we know nothing. After a short period of second childhood, the stars lose all their heat and light-giving powers and become invisible shells of stars. Since we cannot see them, we can only speculate about the number and location of such burnt-out stars.

Over near the southern horizon are more constellations which we should meet. The group of which we speak is to the left of Scorpius and rises a bit later in the evening. Toward the end of autumn when Scorpius has set, it may still be seen on the southern horizon.

First let us look for the short-handled Milk Dipper, so called because the Milky Way runs through it. Though not an accredited constellation it is an easy group to see. When you have found the Milk Dipper you will notice there are a few stars near it, which, when combined

FIG. 45.—The Milk Dipper.

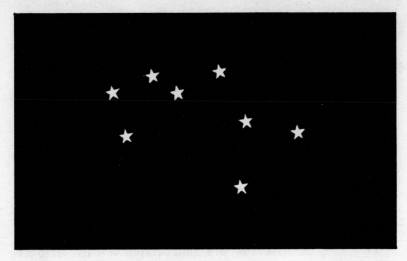

FIG. 46.—The Teapot.

with the stars of the Milk Dipper, make a perfect teapot.. Then, if you ignore two of the stars as you look at the group, you will see the Bow and Arrow which Sagittarius

FIG. 47.—The Bow and Arrow.

FIG. 48.—Great Star Cloud in Sagittarius.

the Archer used. Add a few stars farther away and you will have the complete constellation of Sagittarius the Archer, facing the west with drawn bow and arrow pointed at the Scorpion.

Looking at this group of stars can you pick out the Milk Dipper? Then can you see the Teapot? And the constellation of Sagittarius? They form a very nice group of stars. One of the most impressive parts of the Milky Way is in Sagittarius. This is the great star cloud where, as the great American astronomer Barnard said, "the stars pile up in great cumulus masses, like summer clouds." The center of the galaxy which, as you have learned, is some 30,000 light-years from us, is in the direction of this great star cloud in Sagittarius.

Serpens is a serpent that is about as large as Draco the Dragon. His tail starts above the Teapot in Sagittarius. The head of the serpent is just under the Northern Crown.

Fig. 49.—Sagittarius the Archer and Scorpius.

Fig. 50.—Serpens the Serpent, showing relation to Scorpius, Sagittarius, and Corona.

79

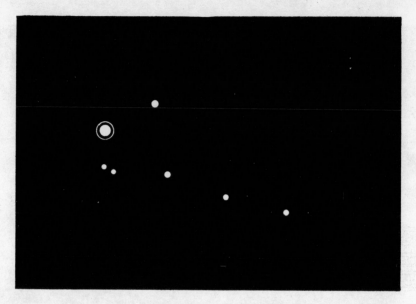

FIG. 51.—Fomalhaut and the Southern Fish.

So lifelike is this constellation that it seems natural to have called it a serpent for over thirty centuries.

The clear and vivid constellations of this part of the sky may well hold our attention up to the first part of November, when at about eight o'clock just above the southern horizon there shines a lone, bright star of the first magnitude. This is Fomalhaut in the mouth of the Southern Fish, a constellation notable only for the presence of this first-magnitude star, which shines without a rival in its part of the sky. It is visible in early evenings in the northern hemisphere only for a very short while in the fall of the year. The greater part of its journey around the polestar is hidden from our sight. Fomalhaut is consequently but little known, and an acquaintance with it definitely places one in the inner circle of stargazers!

7. In the Good Old Wintertime

We have given much attention to the constellations of summer and spring, while perhaps the most gorgeous stars are visible on winter evenings. In much greater degree than in summer, the heavens in winter seem to dazzle us with their brightness. The magnificent company of the winter stars makes its entrance in a most fitting manner. In the east some fall evening, you will see the Pleiades, a sparkling usher to the coming spectacle. They are, some say, the most famous group of stars in the sky. At any rate, they are visible from every inhabited land on the globe.

One's first glimpse of the Pleiades seems to presage their importance, for they are very different in appearance from any other stars in the sky. The Pleiades are a cluster of seemingly tiny stars, glittering and twinkling in the form of a small kite. Using an opera glass, one can distinguish a short-handled dipper among the group. This makes our fifth dipper in the sky. Do you remember the other four?

FIG. 52.—The Pleiades.

FIG. 53.—The Nebula involving the Pleiades.

In the Pleiades one star of the third magnitude and five of the fourth are visible to the average naked eye, although some people with exceptional eyesight can make out a seventh star of the fifth magnitude. A few rare individuals may even make out two more stars of the fifth magnitude—a total of nine in all. With a small telescope more than 100 stars may be seen in the Pleiades, and 2,500 have been counted on a photograph of the cluster. Such photographs show streamer-like nebulae, about which you will read more in a few pages.

As you would expect from their appearance, the stars which make up the Pleiades are a real family group with similar characteristics and a common motion in space.

A Greek legend tells us that the Pleiades were daughters of Atlas and Pleione. The giant hunter Orion saw them one day and admired them. They became frightened and ran away. The hunter followed, for he did not want to lose sight of the beautiful sisters. Orion did not mean to harm them, but the timid Pleiades did not know this, so they appealed to Jupiter for protection. He felt sorry for the sisters and changed them into doves so they were able to fly up into the sky. Later Jupiter made them into a constellation. But even in the sky Orion still seems to be running after the sisters, as on winter evenings he rises above the horizon soon after the Pleiades and strides across the heavens, followed by his dogs.

There are various explanations as to why we can usually see only six Pleiades, when there are supposed to be seven. There are different versions as to which one was lost as well as what happened to the lost one. One tale is that Electra hid so she would not see the fall of Troy. Another story is that she left her place in the sky during the siege in order to see the battle. Unable to return, Electra became the faint star Alcor above the second star in the handle of the Big Dipper. Some other versions say that Pleione is the lost Pleiad. And there are many other versions.

The American Indians had a legend, "The Story of the Hunter and the Seven Dancers," to explain the presence in the sky of the Pleiades. It may be read in *Stars Through Magic Casements.* (See bibliography.)

Around the middle of November the Pleiades are high in the sky at midnight. Many tribes start their year at that time with elaborate ceremonials, and the ancient Persian kings were said to have granted all petitions presented to them then.

About an hour and a half before the Pleiades rise in the east, Capella, one of the most beautiful of the first-magnitude stars, fifth brightest in the heavens, is seen flashing above the northeastern horizon. To the right of it are three smaller stars arranged in a tiny triangle.

Fig. 54.—Capella and the Kids, showing relation to the Pleiades.

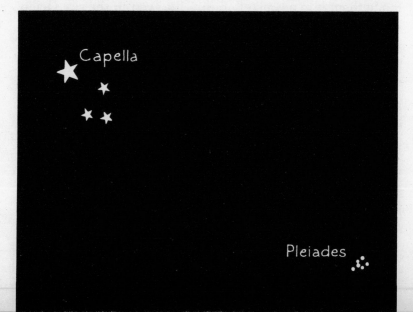

FIG. 55.—The Good Shepherd.

Although the constellation is known as Auriga the Charioteer, Capella, in most legends, is looked on as a goat, and the stars making up the small triangle as her three kids. By adding a few more of the surrounding stars than we used for identification purposes, the ancients saw in the constellation the figure of a man carrying a goat over his back and the kids in his arms.

This constellation is much loved by seamen, and the goats were thought to be on the alert to rescue shipwrecked sailors. Since Capella shines nearly overhead in winter, it is visible in the sky early in the evening when few other stars can be seen and is usually out in stormy weather if any stars are. So it is natural that Capella would seem a friend to seamen. The ancient Hebrews saw in the constellation a representation of the Good Shepherd who was to come and save the world.

About an hour after the Pleiades have risen, a star with a fiery gleam appears over the horizon a bit below the Pleiades. This is Aldebaran, a rosy-red first-magni-

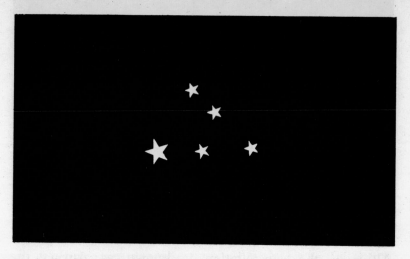

FIG. 56.—Aldebaran and the Hyades form a "V."

tude star in the constellation of Taurus the Bull. You will notice that Aldebaran is in a group of stars shaped like a letter **V** on its side, called the Hyades. The ancients pictured this as a huge bull's head, with Aldebaran as the

FIG. 57.—Taurus the Bull.

animal's blazing eye. The constellation of Taurus is considered by astronomers to include the Pleiades.

As in the case of Cassiopeia, we are unable to understand how one can see anything but a letter of the alphabet in this star group until we see, about 15 degrees to the left, following the direction of each arm of the V, two stars. These are supposed to be the tips of the Bull's horns. While this is a beautiful constellation and readily picked out, it seems difficult to imagine the form of the object for which it is named.

Next in the shining company led by the Pleiades is a constellation which, according to many stargazers, is the finest in the heavens. It is Orion the Hunter. When first looking for this constellation, it is well to wait until the Belt of Orion has risen in the sky just below the Bull. The Belt is made up of three very hot second-magnitude stars on a short, slanting line. Early Christians were said to look upon these stars as the Three Wise Men, ever journeying from the east. To us this has a special significance, since they have a conspicuous place in the evening sky around Christmas.

Below the Belt is a short row of stars hanging downward and representing Orion's Sword. Around the central star in the Sword is the Great Orion Nebula, a large

Fig. 58.—Orion's Belt.   Fig. 59.—Orion's Belt and Sword.

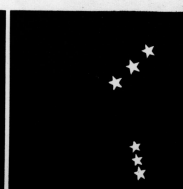

Fig. 60.—Great Gaseous Nebula in Orion.

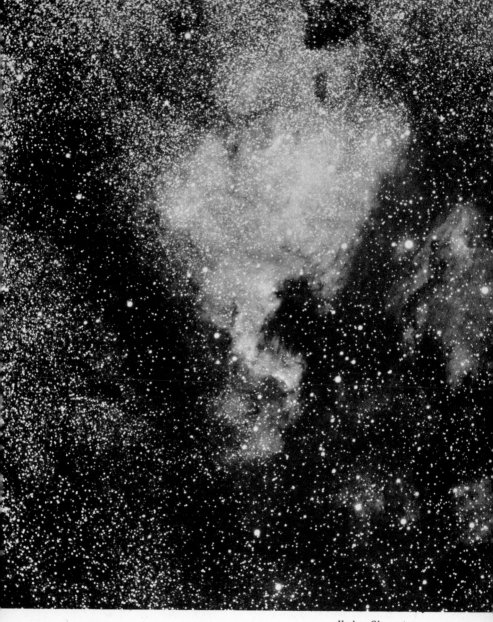

FIG. 61.—North America Nebula, so called because its shape resembles
that of the continent of North America.

89

cloudlike formation as big as the full moon; its brighter parts show a green color in the telescope.

NEBULAE

There are two general types of objects referred to as nebulae. One sort is that which telescopes have shown to be myriads of stars — island universes, or *extra-galactic nebulae* — themselves distant galaxies beyond the confines of our own. The Andromeda Nebula belongs in this class.

Nebulae of the other type are within our own galaxy, and are essentially gaseous. To this class belongs the Great Orion Nebula, surrounding the middle star of Orion's Sword. This nebula, barely perceptible to the naked eye, is the brightest of its class. These gaseous or diffuse nebulae appear in telescopic photographs like glowing, wispy cirrus clouds. In some cases, as in the Pleiades, their light is seen to be reflected star light, for it has the same color as the light from nearby stars. Such nebulae are clouds of dust. Studies of the greenish color of the Orion Nebula and others like it near very hot stars show that they are made of gases which absorb the light of hot stars and glow by fluorescence. Also the planetary nebulae, like the Ring Nebula in Lyra which we have already met, show the same color, and are therefore known to be made up of gas caused to shine by fluorescence in the strong light of nearby hot stars.

Similar to these vast diffuse nebulae are the dark clouds in the Milky Way, which are large masses of gas and dust with no bright stars nearby. They shield the more distant stars from our view, and appear in the sky as dark

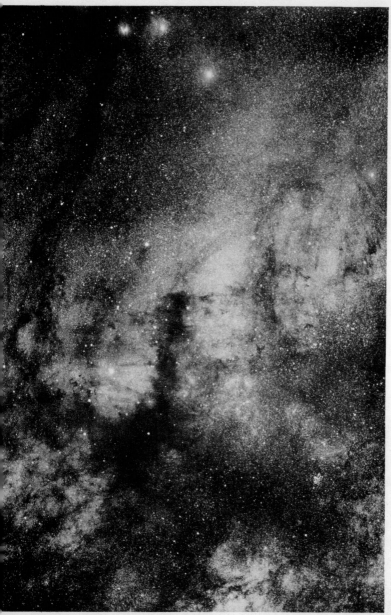

Fig. 62.—Milky Way in Sagittarius, showing obscuring dark clouds.

91

patches (see Figure 62). Sometimes they have bright edges where there are stars nearby, as in the region around the "Gulf of Mexico" in the "North American Nebula," illustrated in Figure 61.

Since the two main types of nebulae—"island universes" and gaseous nebulae within our own galaxy — are so different, one may wonder why they share the same name. (In fact, at one time star clusters, like that in Hercules, were also considered nebulae.) The answer is that to the eye and even to the small telescope they look alike, and only the larger telescopes show their true differences.

After you have found the Belt and Sword of Orion, you will be able to find the remaining stars making up the figure. Four stars forming a figure almost rectangular in shape surround it, two being of the first magnitude, and the other two, like those in the Belt, being of the second magnitude. Betelgeuse, to the ancients, was the ruby pin fastening Orion's lionskin on his right shoulder. The

FIG. 63.—Orion.

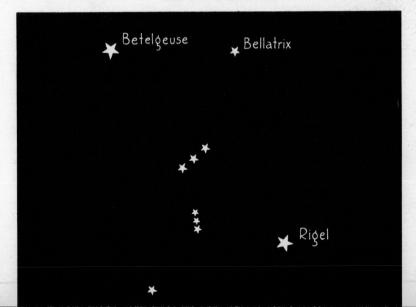

modern astronomer sees in its red color and brilliance the fact that it is a relatively cool star and very, very large. It is of historical interest because it is the first star whose diameter was measured directly. Betelgeuse is so large that the earth's orbit would easily fit inside it! It may surprise you that large telescopes do not magnify the sizes of stars; they only make them much brighter. This is because the stars are so very far away that even one as big as Betelgeuse, magnified by the 200-inch telescope, shows as only a microscopic point of light. A special instrument had to be made to measure the diameter, and it works only on the largest stars.

Rigel, also of the first magnitude, is a bluish-white star, a buckle on Orion's left shoe (the other presumably having been lost!). From its bluish color we see that it is a very hot star, as are the stars of the Belt and Sword. You will remember that it is the high temperatures of the latter stars which cause the Orion Nebula to fluoresce with its greenish color.

Bellatrix, the second-magnitude star forming Orion's left shoulder, is one to which astrologers have attached special interest. The superstition was long believed that women born when this star is in the sky possess sharp tongues and can speak up for themselves. It may be appropriate to state at this point that, for us, Bellatrix is above the horizon about half the time!

Since such a splendid constellation was named after him, we can be sure that Orion was a great hero of some sort, but his actual identity is a good bit of a mystery. All stories agree that he was the mightiest hunter ever known;

and we can only hope that this is true, for Taurus the Bull, with fiery eye and immense — if unconvincing — horns, seems charging at him in such a manner that we cannot help feeling some concern for his safety!

Orion is such a beautiful constellation that many great conquerors have sent out decrees that the constellation be renamed for them. These names have never lasted, even though they have been proposed by men much more real to us than the mythical Orion — Alexander and Napoleon being among them. It is interesting to wonder if any of our modern dictators ever wished to have Orion proclaim their greatness from the heavens.

I once heard an elderly minister regret that he had never been able to visit the Holy Land and walk among the hills and through the countryside where the people of the Bible had lived. Every winter night he can look on natural objects familiar to and beloved by these people. The stars held an important place in the lives of the Biblical folks, and especially was Orion beloved by them. Often in the Bible we find mention of the stars, and sometimes of definite constellations. Job, when speaking of the glories of God (Job IX: 8, 9) says: "Which alone spreadeth out the heavens, and treadeth upon the waves of the sea. Which maketh Arcturus, Orion, and Pleiades . . . ."

We need not have worried over Orion's safety, since in an hour or so he has chased Taurus the Bull until he is halfway up the eastern sky. By that time our attention has been called away from him, for, on the horizon below flames Sirius, the Dog Star, brightest of all the stars.

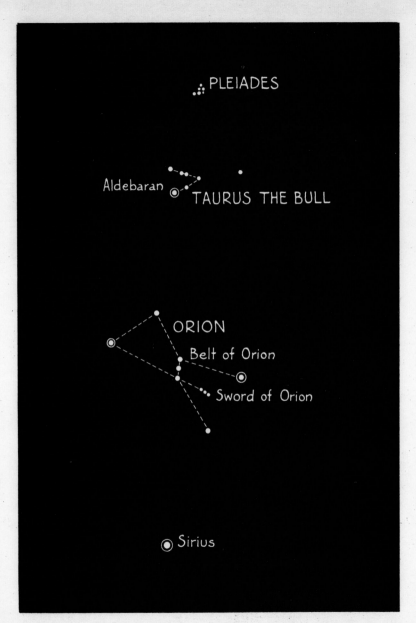

FIG. 64.—Sirius in relation to Orion, Taurus, and the Pleiades.

"... see him mount the eastern sky,
Eagerly, with a sort of joy of shining,
A flickering silver flame,
All gleaming, darting points of spiny light—
Sirius, the dancing star,
The winter-rising."
      —DOLORES CAIRNS, *Christian Science Monitor*

To call Sirius a first-magnitude star seems an injustice. In brightness Sirius is so far superior to all the others, it seems to stand alone in its magnificence. Its light is bluish-white. Just after it comes over the horizon on a clear night you can see it twinkle in many colors (as do all the stars, the brightest ones most noticeably). This effect is due to the earth's atmosphere and is like the "shimmering" you sometimes see looking across the top of a hot stove. When you look at a star on the horizon you are looking through a lot of air just above the warm surface of the earth.

Even though it is so bright, Sirius is not the nearest visible star. The star enjoying that distinction (not counting the sun, of course) is in the Centaur, a southern constellation near Scorpius which you will not ordinarily see. The brightest star in the Centaur, Alpha Centauri, a brilliant first-magnitude star, is the nearest one visible to the naked eye. During the early evenings of July and August it may be seen, low on the horizon, from the extreme southern parts of the United States. It is about four light-years away. Slightly nearer is the fainter star Proxima Centauri, visible only through a telescope. Of course, there may be other closer stars, fainter and as yet undiscovered. Such close, faint stars are truly dwarfs, and if we were to swap one for our sun the earth would be a very cold place indeed.

Twenty-one stars all nearer than a dozen light-years are known, and all but Sirius, Alpha Centauri, and Procyon (see Figure 65) are very small stars. Sirius is somewhat less than nine light-years distant; if it were to blow up like a nova we wouldn't see the explosion until nine years after it had happened.

Sirius is a blue star and therefore very hot. Its true brilliance is about twenty-seven times that of our sun. If Sirius were to be placed in the position of our "Old Sol," all the earth's seas would boil away. And yet, Sirius is far from being the greatest of the stars! It is approaching us at the rate of about 4 miles per second—about 100 million miles a year—but its appearance in the sky will not change for thousands of years. In a thousand years it will be only one-sixtieth of a light-year closer, and its appearance in the sky will be changed very little.

Such a conspicuous object could scarcely fail to become associated with earthly affairs. The Egyptians called Sirius the Nile star because when it appeared in the sky just before dawn, the season for the rising of the Nile had come. A connection was imagined between the two events. Sirius is called the Dog Star, because it is part of a constellation called the Big Dog—not an easy one to pick out, except possibly when Orion is setting in the west on spring evenings, when the Dog may be seen trailing him along the western horizon. At the time of year when Sirius

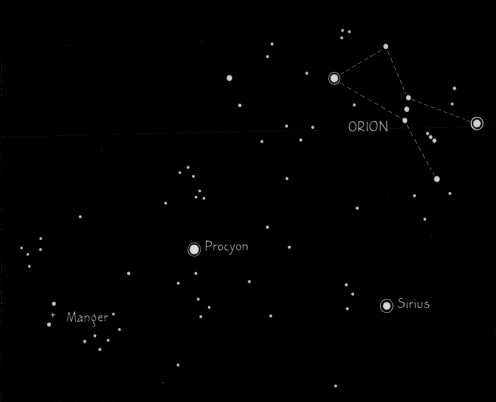

FIG. 65.—Procyon in relation to Orion and the Manger.

rises with the sun (August) we usually have very hot weather; the days of this sultry period are called the "dog days." Sirius is, of course, a disinterested party.

Between Orion and the Manger, which we mentioned among the springtime stars, is Procyon, a lonely first-magnitude star, golden yellow, and known as the "Little Dog Star." With it are smaller stars which very faintly suggest the outline of a dog, which in most legends is said to be Orion's, but is sometimes spoken of as one of Diana's hunting dogs. Do you remember the Summer Triangle, which is so prominent in the northeast sky on summer evenings? Procyon, Sirius, and Betelgeuse form a star group which we may call the Winter Triangle. It has almost equal sides and is about the same size as the Summer Triangle, but is in the southeastern sky on winter evenings.

Among the many inhabitants of the sky are the twins, Castor and Pollux, who spend all their winter evenings with us. They were twin sons of Jupiter and patrons of sports, Castor favoring horsemanship while Pollux was most fond of boxing. Castor, a mortal, was slain in battle, and Jupiter, in order to comfort the grieving twin, Pollux, who was immortal, put them both in the sky together.

Both the Greeks and the Romans regarded Castor and Pollux as patrons of navigation. After St. Paul's disas-

FIG. 66.—The Winter Triangle.

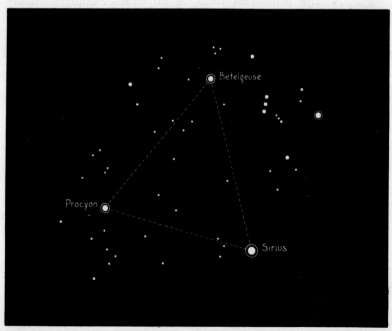

FIG. 67.—Castor and Pollux, the Heavenly Twins, in relation to Procyon and Betelgeuse.

trous shipwreck on the island of Melita, now known as Malta, he continued his voyage to Rome in a ship bearing the name of these twin stars (Acts XXVIII: 11).

Pollux, the immortal twin, is an orange-colored, first-magnitude star, while Castor is almost as bright, a white star in whose rays some observers can see a hint of green. To these two chief stars are added a few smaller surrounding ones, making two "stick men" figures of the friendly-looking brothers. The whole constellation is gemmed with stars that escape the eye, but which, when viewed through an opera glass, sparkle like diamond dust. Our imaginations are overwhelmed with the immensity of the universe when we realize that each "speck of star dust" is a sun.

FIRST-MAGNITUDE STARS IN ORDER OF BRIGHTNESS

Order	Star	Constellation (English Name)	Constellation (Latin Name)	Color	Light-Years Away
1	Sirius	Great Dog	Canis Major	Blue	8.6
2	*Canopus	Keel	Carina	Yellow-white	100
3	*Alpha Centauri (Rigil Kentaurus)	Centaur	Centaurus	Yellow	4.3
4	Vega	Lyre	Lyra	Blue	26
5	Capella	Charioteer	Auriga	Yellow	42
6	Arcturus	Herdsman, or Bear Driver	Boötes	Reddish	33
7	Rigel	Orion	Orion	Blue-white	540
8	Procyon	Little Dog	Canis Minor	Yellow-white	11.1
9	*Achernar	A River	Eridanus	Blue-white	70
10	*Beta Centauri	Centaur	Centaurus	Blue-white	190
11	Altair	Eagle	Aquila	Blue	15.7
12	Betelgeuse	Orion	Orion	Red	300
13	*Alpha Crucis (Acrux)	Cross, or Southern Cross	Crux	Blue-white	220
14	Aldebaran	Bull	Taurus	Reddish	53
15	Spica	Virgin	Virgo	Blue-white	120
16	Pollux	Twins	Gemini	Reddish	29
17	Antares	Scorpion	Scorpius, or Scorpio	Red	250
18	Fomalhaut	Southern Fish	Piscis Austrinis	Blue	23
19	Deneb	Swan, or Northern Cross	Cygnus	Blue	400
20	Regulus	Lion	Leo	Blue	67

* Not visible at 40 degrees north latitude. These are typically Southern Hemisphere stars, but can be seen at times from the southern to the extreme southern parts of the United States. Canopus is visible south of about 37 degrees north latitude, or about the latitude of Nashville. Achernar can be seen south of about 32 degrees north latitude, or about the latitude of Mobile. But to see Alpha Centauri and Beta Centauri, which are visible south of about 29 degrees north latitude, one must be as far south as central Florida or southern Texas. And to see Alpha Crucis, which is visible south of about 27 degrees north latitude, one must be in the southern part of Florida or the extreme southern part of Texas.

8. Our Solar System

Perhaps when you were out stargazing, you noticed, in a conspicuous part of the sky, a bright star which we failed to mention. Maybe you became interested enough to watch it for a few nights and found that it did not keep the same position in relation to the other stars, but seemed to move among them. You were seeing a planet, for four of them, Venus, Mars, Jupiter, and Saturn, may easily be seen at certain times. (The word "planet" comes from a Greek word meaning "wanderer.")

In trying to identify them it may help to remember that, although the stars seem to twinkle, planets usually shine steadily. Stars twinkle because the air is moving. It makes them shimmer—more when the star is near the horizon than when it is overhead. This shimmering of the light from the stars, which, as we have seen, are but points of light even in the largest telescopes, sometimes makes them seem to go off and on. On the other hand, the planets, which are much nearer to us, appear as disks rather than points in a telescope. All parts of the disks twinkle, but they do not twinkle together so the planet appears to shine with a steady light.

It is interesting to realize that the planets do not shine by their own light as do the sun and the other stars, but merely reflect light from the sun. This is very obvious in the case of the moon. Observers on the other planets would see the earth reflecting light coming from the sun.

The planets follow roughly the same path in the heavens as do the sun and moon. Thus they are always in the zodiac which crosses the southern part of our sky. You can be absolutely sure that you will never see any planet near the Big Dipper or in Corona. In order to find what planets are in the sky when you go stargazing, you should consult the monthly star maps which appear in *Nature Magazine, Popular Astronomy, Science News Letter,* or the *Monthly Evening Sky Map.* If you wish to know the exact position and time of rising of the planets day by day, a copy of the *Old Farmers' Almanac* for the current year will be of value. *A Beginner's Star-Book* by McKready lists the constellations in which each of the visible planets will appear to be, up to the year 1955.

On most of the planet charts you will see that they are spoken of as being "in" certain constellations. This is merely a figure of speech, for the stars of the constellations are very much farther from us than the planets. The planets revolve in their orbits around our sun with the stars as background. If we find Venus, for instance, moving between us and Virgo, with the stars of Virgo as a background, we say that Venus is in Virgo, for the planet seems to be among its stars.

We have seen that, as the earth moves around the sun, the sun appears in different constellations (see Figure 43), that is, besides its daily rising and setting, it moves completely around the sky among the stars in one year. It was supposed by the ancients that this motion was due to the sun revolving around the earth. To them it did not

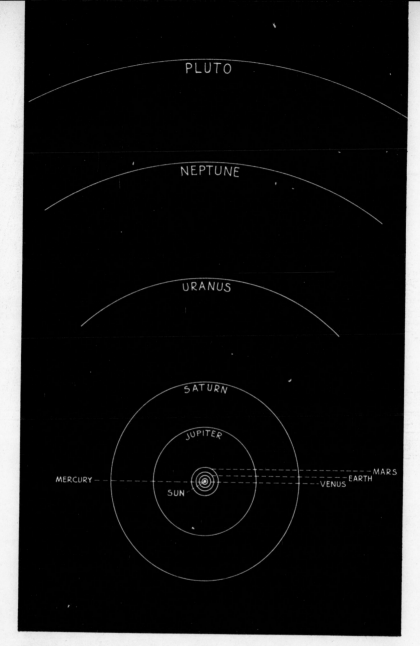

FIG. 68.—Orbits of the planets of our solar system, drawn to approximate scale.

seem possible that any other body could be greater than the earth, or that the seemingly motionless earth could be moving around anything. But since the time of Copernicus, about 1550, it has been well established that the earth does the revolving, rather than the sun, and that the eight other planets, some smaller, some larger than the earth, also go around the much larger sun, all moving in the same direction. With the exception of Pluto and Mercury, their paths are all practically circular and all very nearly in the same plane. The orbits of Pluto and Mercury are somewhat elongated and inclined to that of the earth.

Two of the planets—Mercury and Venus—are nearer the sun than we, and so, of course, have smaller orbits (shorter paths around the sun) and complete their journeys around the sun in a shorter time than does the earth. Since a year on a planet is the time it takes to make a complete revolution around the sun, a year on either of these planets is shorter than a year on earth: the Mercurian year is only about one fourth the length of our year. On the other hand, the more remote planets move in such large orbits that immense intervals of time are taken up in their journeys around the sun.

Besides the motion of each planet in its path around the sun, each turns about an axis just as the earth turns on its axis daily from west to east. This rotation leads to days and nights on the other planets, also of different lengths than our days and nights on the earth.

The nine planets in the order of their distances from the sun are: Mercury, Venus, Earth, Mars, Jupiter, Saturn, Uranus, Neptune, and Pluto.

After the name of each planet below is given the standard symbol used to indicate it on charts and maps and in almanacs. On the right side of the page is a circle showing the relative size. As you read about each planet, you will find it interesting to compare its size and distance from the sun with the others. Since the paths of the earth and the other planets are not true circles around the sun, the distances from the sun given for each are average distances. For each planet the length of day and length of year are given in earth days and years. Everybody knows that the earth has just one moon; some of the planets have not one but as many as thirteen moons, and two certainly have no moons at all. To distinguish these from our moon they are generally called satellites.

MERCURY ☿

Distance from sun:	36 million miles	o
Diameter of planet:	3,000 miles	
Length of day:	88 days	Relative size in
Length of year:	88 days	comparison with
Satellites:	None	the other planets

Mercury, the fastest moving planet, is aptly named, since in mythology Mercury was the fleet messenger of the gods. Among the planets it enjoys the distinction of being the smallest, the closest to the sun, and therefore the hottest.

Mercury makes one rotation on its axis in the same time that it makes one revolution around the sun. This not only means that its day and year are of the same length, but that the same side of the planet is always toward the sun. One side enjoys perpetual day, the other perpetual night. Since it is so near the sun, it receives much more light and heat than our earth. But only the side facing the sun can take advantage of this. This side has a temperature of about 770 degrees (lead melts at 621 degrees), while the other part is always frozen. Therefore, life—as we know it here on the earth—would be impossible on this planet.

Mercury is so small that, like our moon, it has no atmosphere. Very likely, when this planet was formed, it had its share of the gases that make up an atmosphere, but because of its small size it did not have sufficient gravity to hold them. To illustrate the ease with which the fast-moving particles of gas which made up the atmosphere escaped, we may note that the force of gravity on Mercury is so weak that a man who on earth can lift a 50-pound weight with one hand, could lift 185 pounds on Mercury with equal ease. There a mere amateur could jump five feet just as easily as he can step off a curb on our earth.

Because Mercury is so close to the sun, this planet is difficult to see. Occasionally, however, when its appearance is scheduled, an attentive observer may see it near the western horizon shortly after sunset, or on the eastern horizon shortly before sunrise. For a few days the planet comes out far enough from the sun to be easily visible. Since it never gets farther than 28 degrees east or west of the sun, Mercury cannot be seen throughout the night; but, by carefully shading their telescopes from the sunlight, astronomers are able to observe it during the daylight hours whenever it is far enough away from the sun.

As seen through a telescope, Mercury passes through changes in appearance somewhat like those of our moon. When on the other side of the sun from us it is full. As it comes around the sun closer to the earth, the part we see illuminated changes gradually to a crescent; then it almost disappears, as the planet passes between the sun and the earth.

About thirteen times in a century Mercury crosses exactly between the earth and the sun. It may then be seen through a telescope as a black dot crossing the disk of the sun. This does not cause a solar eclipse because Mercury is so small that it obscures only a tiny part of the sun's disk. This is called a *transit* of Mercury. Transits of Mercury are infrequent because the inclination of Mercury's orbit to the orbit of the earth causes it usually to go above or below the sun as it swings around between the sun and the earth. There will be seven more such transits between now and the year 2000. They always occur in May or November: the next three are scheduled for November, 1953; May, 1957; and November, 1960.

The early Greeks had two names for this planet. When it was in the evening sky, they called it Mercury, as we do. But when they saw it in the morning sky, they did not recognize it as the same planet they had seen about two months earlier in the evening sky, and gave it the name of Apollo. Later Greek astronomers discovered that the planet they saw in the east was identical with the one they saw in the west.

VENUS ♀

Distance from sun: 67 million miles
Diameter of planet: 7,600 miles
Length of day: Undetermined
Length of year: 225 days
Satellites: None

○

Relative size in comparison with the other planets

With the exception of the sun and moon, the brilliant white Venus, named for the goddess of beauty, is the most conspicuous object in the sky. Only a very bright comet or a particularly brilliant nova exceeds it in brightness. At its brightest, Venus is about ten times as bright as Sirius, our brightest star, and four or five times as bright as Mars or Jupiter. When Venus is above the horizon at night, it will sometimes cast a shadow.

Because Venus goes around the sun closer than the earth it is never farther than 47 degrees east or west of the sun in the sky as seen from the earth, and so can never be seen in the middle of the night. It sometimes shines for nearly three hours after sunset in the western sky, when it is called the Evening Star, subject of song and poetry, or for three hours before sunrise in the eastern sky, when it is called the Morning Star. The ancient Greeks had two names for Venus, just as for Mercury: as a morning star it was called Phosphoros; as an evening star, Hesperus. When it is farthest east or west of the sun, Venus can easily be seen in a clear, daylight sky, and has often been mistaken for a "flying saucer" or some other unnatural object. But you will have trouble in finding it in daytime unless you know exactly where it is.

Like Mercury, Venus presents different phases: cres-

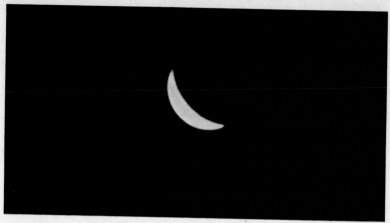

Yerkes Observatory

FIG. 69.—Venus, showing crescent phase.

cent, full planet, etc. They may be seen through a small field glass. When Venus is at the farther part of its orbit —beyond the sun from us and 160 million miles away—we see it as a full planet. As it comes nearer us in its journey along its orbit, its disk appears larger and larger, but we see only a smaller portion of it lighted. After reaching its maximum brightness in this crescent phase, the planet then gets fainter as it swings between us and the sun, where we see only its dark side. As it continues in its orbit going away from us, it passes through the same changes again until it may finally be seen as a full planet again on the other side of the sun.

Venus actually makes one complete trip around the sun in 225 days. But we cannot stay in one place to observe Venus. Instead, we must move with the earth, going around the sun in 365 days. Thus, because both planets are moving, about 584 days elapse from one full planet to the next.

Like Mercury, Venus usually passes above or below the sun, but it does have transits, although they are less frequent than those of Mercury. The last two were in December, 1874, and December, 1882. The next two will not come till June, 2004, and June, 2012. Put 2004 on your calendar, for a transit of Venus is worth seeing!

Venus is the planet most like our earth and is sometimes referred to as our sister planet. It is about the same size as the earth. Although Venus comes closer to us than any other planet, we know very little about it, for it has a very dense atmosphere and is covered with heavy clouds. Because these clouds obscure surface markings, we do not know how long it takes to make one rotation on it axis —that is, we do not know the length of a day on Venus. Only very small amounts of oxygen and water vapor appear to be present in the planet's upper atmosphere, but it contains large amounts of carbon dioxide.

Venus is much closer to the sun than we are. Because of this it completes its journey around the sun in a much shorter period, and hence its year is much shorter than ours. It receives about twice as much heat and light from the sun as we do. Its surface temperature is undoubtedly high, but some parts of it may have a temperate climate. It has been suggested that millions of years ago, when our earth is believed to have been much warmer than it is now, conditions here may have been very much like those on Venus today. Thus it is not impossible that some form of life may yet develop, or now be in the process of developing, on Venus. At least, we cannot rule out this possibility until we know more about the planet's surface.

EARTH ⊕

Distance from sun:	93,003,000 miles
Diameter of planet:	7,918 miles
Length of day:	24 hours
Length of year:	365¼ days
Satellites:	1 large

○

Relative size in comparison with the other planets

The size of the earth is not distinctive, there being both larger and smaller planets; its position is not unusual, for there are two planets nearer the sun, and six beyond it. The feature which makes our earth unique is the presence of our form of life upon it. Most scientists agree that we find life on our planet because conditions are right for it. The earth's size and the sort of materials that make it up cause its gravity, or holding power, to strike a happy medium. It is not too great for living creatures such as men to exist, nor is it so small that it cannot hold sufficient atmosphere to support life. Its relatively temperate climate is due to the fact that it is neither extremely far from nor extremely near to the sun. A layer of ozone in our upper atmosphere screens out most of the sun's ultraviolet light, which would otherwise kill living cells.

FIG. 70.—The curvature of the earth is clearly shown by this mosaic made up of separate photographs shot by an automatic camera in a V-2 rocket on July 26, 1948, at approximately 50 miles above the surface of the earth. The area photographed is 1,400 miles from south to north. The numbers indicate towns and other geographic features, as follows: (1) Mexico, (2) Gulf of California, (3) Lordsburg, New Mexico, (4) Peloncillo Mountains, (5) Gila River, (6) San Carlos Reservoir, (7) Magellen Mountains, (8) Balck Range, (9) San Mateo Mountains, (10) Magdalena Mountains, (11) Mount Taylor, (12) Albuquerque, New Mexico, (13) Sandia Mountains, (14) Valle Grande Mountains, (15) Rio Grande River, (16) Sangre de Cristo Range.

Official U.S. Navy Photograph

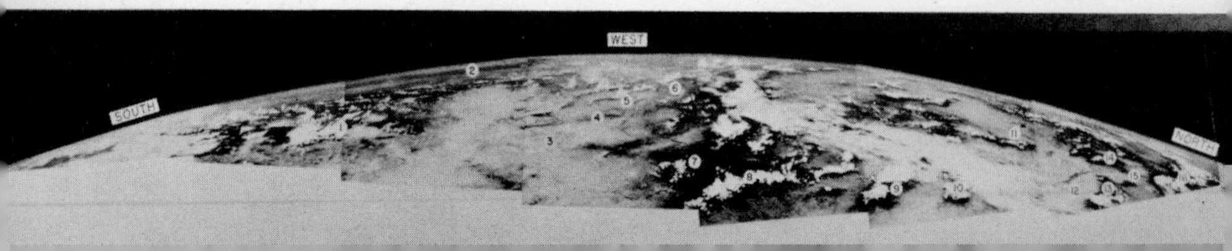

MARS ♂

Distance from sun:	142 million miles
Diameter of planet:	4,220 miles
Length of day:	24 hr. 37 min.
Length of year:	687 days
Satellites:	2

o

Relative size in comparison with the other planets

Mars, named after the mythical god of war, is the best known to us of all the other planets. Its fiery red color reminds one of Antares, whose name indeed means "rival of Mars." It is not hard to recognize from this ruddy color, but once you find it, remember that the motion of Mars among the stars is so rapid that it will move into a different constellation of the zodiac in at most two months.

Mars varies enormously in brilliance, being sometimes forty times as bright as Antares; at its dimmest it is only about second magnitude. Unlike Venus, which shows less of its lighted surface as it passes closest to the earth (between us and the sun), the whole near side of Mars is lighted up when it is nearest us (the earth then being between Mars and the sun). In fact, the disk of Mars as seen through a telescope is never very much less than fully illuminated by the sun, so that its brightness depends principally upon its distance from the earth and from the sun. When it is closest to the earth (and brightest) Mars is about 35,000,000 miles away. But when it is on the opposite side of the sun from us, Mars is about seven times farther away and consequently about fifty times fainter. Moreover, the orbit of Mars is much less circular than the orbit of the earth. You will remember that the earth's distance from the sun varies by 3,000,000 miles; the distance of Mars from the sun varies by 26,000,000 miles during its year, and this also causes some changes in brightness.

When the earth, which moves faster in its orbit, passes Mars every 26 months, we get a fairly close view; but every fifteen years or so we pass Mars on the part of its orbit closest to the sun, and at these times conditions for observing Mars are particularly favorable. The next opportunity of this kind will be about 1954. At such a time in 1877 the two satellites and the canals of Mars were first reported. In August, 1924, we had a much closer view of Mars than we shall have again for several centuries. At that time Mars was brighter than Jupiter ever becomes.

Mars has two moons, Phobos and Deimos (Fear and Panic), named after two of the sons and companions of the god of war. They are among the smallest of the known heavenly bodies, Phobos being 10 or 15 miles in diameter, and Deimos about half as large. Phobos goes around Mars in less than eight hours, making its "month" less than a third of a day on Mars! To an observer on Mars, Phobos would appear to rise in the west and set in the east.

Since Mars comes quite near the earth and has a relatively thin atmosphere, its surface is the most studied of all the planets. The clearest features are the polar caps— white mantles of frost around both the north pole and the south pole of the planet—which are seen to grow larger in the winter of each hemisphere. Around the equator of Mars there is a dark belt which spreads toward each pole during the Martian summer. Professor Kuiper of Yerkes Observatory, from studies of the light reflected from these areas, has suggested that they may be lichen-like growths,

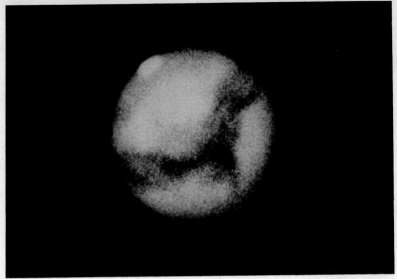

FIG. 71.—Mars, showing one polar cap and dark green band.

but others have suggested some form of life different from any known on earth, or even chemical changes not involving any living matter, caused by changes in moisture and temperature conditions.

The much publicized "canals" on Mars are not easily seen, even in the most powerful telescopes, although some careful observers have reported fleeting glimpses of a network of fine, straight, dark lines, running between the green belt and the polar caps. They have never shown on photographs, possibly because of the twinkling mentioned at the beginning of this chapter. Therefore, their existence is not completely accepted by astronomers.

Even if the "canals" are verified, it will not be proved that they are artificial or "man-made"; they would more likely be natural features. The whole question of life on

Mars has fired the imagination of astronomers and others for many years. It is now being seriously studied through the conditions under which life would have to exist there. The temperature on Mars is much lower than that found on the earth because it is farther from the sun and therefore receives much less heat than does our planet. However, careful calculations and measurements have shown that it is warmer than freezing during the daytime near the Martian equator.

Besides a suitable temperature, another requirement for life as we know it is oxygen. Although many astronomers have tried to detect oxygen in Mars's atmosphere, there seems to be almost none of this gas there. Moreover, without oxygen there would be no ozone in Mars's atmosphere, and the sun's sterilizing ultraviolet rays, from which we are protected by ozone in the earth's atmosphere, would tend to kill all ordinary living matter on Mars. There are certainly no oceans on Mars; the total amount of water is very small, and it is probably mostly in the form of ice or frost in the polar caps.

JUPITER ♃

Distance from sun: 483 million miles
Diameter of planet: 88,640 miles
Length of day: 9 hr. 50 min.
Length of year: 12 years
Satellites: 13

Relative size in comparison with the other planets

Even as Jupiter was king of the gods, so his namesake is "king of the planets," larger and heavier than all the other planets combined. The volume of this planet is about 1300 times that of the earth. Its diameter is one

Yerkes Observatory

FIG. 72.—Jupiter, showing belts or bands on the planet's surface which are probably clouds of gas in Jupiter's atmosphere.

tenth that of the sun. Jupiter is more than five times as far from the sun as the earth is, and its surface temperature is about 220 degrees below zero. It takes 12 years to go around the sun, thus remaining in the same constellation about a year, where it can be recognized by its brilliance and steady golden light. When opposite the sun in the sky, and therefore closest to us, it is ten times brighter than Capella, which is almost the same color. It does not change much in brightness, dropping to about five times as bright as Capella when beyond the sun. It is curious that, in spite of its great size, Jupiter rotates faster than any of the other planets—so much faster that a day on Jupiter is less than half as long as our day.

Jupiter has thirteen moons. Two of the larger ones are larger than the planet Mercury, and two are about the size of our moon. The smaller ones are less than 100 miles in diameter, and can be photographed with large telescopes only. But if you have a good pair of field glasses you can see the four larger moons, just as did the great Italian scientist, Galileo, in 1610, with the first telescope. As Galileo watched Jupiter with his crude telescope for several nights he was amazed to see these four small "stars," as they appeared to him, move from one side of Jupiter to the other. He soon recognized that they were moving around Jupiter in orbits, and used this to argue that the earth and planets moved around the sun in a similar way. These four Galilean satellites have a modern use to navigators. Since they are easily seen with a small telescope and move around Jupiter in periods between two and sixteen days, they form nature's own clock in the sky, from which a man-made clock can be set, no matter where it is. Navigators' tables show the exact times throughout the year when each of these moons disappears behind Jupiter.

In a telescope the disk of Jupiter is seen to be flattened by the high rotational speed, and the edges of the planet are darker than the center, as shown in Figure 72. We have never seen the solid surface, but there are bands of clouds in stripes around the planet parallel to the equator.

118

A study of the reflected light shows that Jupiter's atmosphere is composed mainly of hydrogen, methane, ammonia, and the clouds are probably made up of small drops of the last two substances. In fact, the surface of the planet is probably covered with liquid ammonia and methane at low temperatures several hundred miles below the clouds, and therefore unsuitable for any form of life. Beneath the liquid ammonia there may be a layer of ice. Only a small core of the planet is believed to be composed of rock.

SATURN ♄

Distance from sun:	886 million miles
Diameter of planet:	74,000 miles
Length of day:	10 hr. 14 min.
Length of year:	29½ years
Satellites:	11

Relative size in comparison with the other planets

Saturn, sixth planet from the sun, marked the boundary of the solar system for the ancients. With a small telescope you can see its three concentric rings around the equator, vast in extent, very thin, and differing from everything else in the solar system. These rings appear solid, but in reality, are composed of myriads of particles, each in its own orbit. It is thought that these particles are fragments of a former moon which got too close to Saturn and was broken up by its strong gravitational force. Saturn's present moons are all small, and can only be seen through a large telescope. Saturn is almost as large as Jupiter, and, except for the rings, very similar to it. Bands of clouds also appear on its surface, and it is also flattened by its fast rotation.

The density of Saturn is so low that it would float in water—if there were a body of water large enough to hold it. It has been suggested that half of Saturn's apparent size is due to its deep atmosphere.

The temperature of Saturn—about 243 degrees below zero—is, of course, lower than that of Jupiter, since it is almost twice as far from the sun. This great distance also results in its being fainter than Jupiter. Life, as we know it, would be impossible on this or other planets farther from the sun.

Saturn appears as a large yellow "star." You will find it near the same constellation for a long time. Because of its long path around the sun, along which it moves the slowest planet visible to the naked eye, Saturn spends about two and one-half years in each constellation of the zodiac.

FIG. 73.—Saturn, showing the rings that revolve about the planet.

Yerkes Observatory

URANUS ♅

Distance from sun: 1,782 million miles
Diameter of planet: 32,000 miles
Length of day: 10 hr. 45 min.
Length of year: 84 years
Satellites: 5

Relative size in comparison with the other planets

The planet Uranus, named for the Greek god of the heavens, the father of all the gods, can be seen with the aid of a telescope. It is of sixth magnitude and although barely visible to the naked eye on a good night, it could not be distinguished from a faint star.

Sir William Herschel discovered it in 1781. He was a musician, but spent all his spare time studying astronomy. He could not afford to buy a telescope, so he made his own. Soon he was making better telescopes than anyone else, and

Fig. 74.—Uranus and its five satellites. The minute dot near the upper right-hand portion of the planet is the satellite Miranda, discovered on February 15, 1948. It is about 81,000 miles from Uranus. The peculiar appearance of Uranus itself is due to overexposure in this photograph, necessary in order to record the faint satellites. Photographs of the planet with shorter exposure time reveal it as an almost spherical body, similar in shape to the other planets.

Yerkes Observatory

became very expert in their use. (You will recall that Herschel is the astronomer who first gave us a picture of our galaxy by studying the Milky Way and the Great Nebula in Andromeda.) After George III, king of England during our Revolutionary War, made him Astronomer Royal, Herschel gave up music for astronomy. He first named his new planet after George III, but the name was later dropped in favor of the name Uranus.

Since the distance of Uranus from the sun is twice that of Saturn, Herschel's discovery doubled the diameter of the known solar system. Uranus moves slowly in this large orbit around the sun; by 1945 it had completed only two revolutions around the sun since its discovery.

The solid surface of Uranus, like those of Jupiter and Saturn, is hidden from us by a thick, cloudy atmosphere of

FIG. 75.—Neptune and its first-known satellite, Triton. The second-known satellite, Nereid, which was not discovered until 1949, is too faint to show in this photograph. Triton is 220,000 miles from Neptune, and Nereid is about sixteen times farther away.

Yerkes Observatory

methane and other gases. Its temperature is about 300 degrees below zero. Its rotation and the plane of its satellites' orbits are unusual in being almost perpendicular to the plane of its orbit. Uranus' fifth satellite, the one closest to the planet, was discovered in 1948 by Professor Kuiper of the Yerkes Observatory, using the 82-inch telescope at the McDonald Observatory in Texas.

NEPTUNE ♆

Distance from sun:	2,793 million miles
Diameter of planet:	32,000 miles
Length of day:	15 hr. 48 min.
Length of year:	165 years
Satellites:	2

Relative size in comparison with the other planets

A century ago, when Uranus was thought to be the outermost planet of the sun's family, astronomers had calculated the path it ought to follow, taking account of the gravitational pulls of the sun and all the other known planets. They found that it did not keep strictly to this predicted orbit, and began to suspect that there must be some planet, as yet undiscovered, with an orbit beyond Uranus, pulling that planet out of its course. In 1890, a young mathematician, J. C. Adams of Cambridge, England, computed where and of what size a new planet would have to be if its gravitational pull were to account for Uranus' wanderings. However, none of the English astronomers would believe him! Meanwhile, however, Leverrier, a French astronomer in Paris, had come to the same conclusion. He got a German astronomer named Galle to look through a sufficiently large telescope at the predicted place in the sky, where a planet was discovered almost exactly in the position which both Adams and Leverrier had predicted. It is known as Neptune, named for the god of the sea.

Neptune is of the eighth magnitude—bright enough to be seen with good field glasses, although a larger telescope is necessary to distinguish it from a star. The distance of Neptune from the sun exceeds the combined distances, great as they are, of Saturn and Uranus from the sun. It is very like Uranus in size and atmosphere, and its low temperature of 330 degrees below zero is not surprising at its great distance from the sun; from Neptune the sun would appear to be about the size that Venus appears to us, although about a million times brighter. Not until the year 2011 will Neptune be back to the place in its orbit where it was discovered.

Neptune's rotation is fast, like Jupiter's, Saturn's, and Uranus'. Its equator, and the plane of its larger satellite's orbit, are close to the plane of Neptune's orbit about the sun. In 1949 Professor Kuiper discovered the second, smaller satellite, the farther one from the planet.

PLUTO ♇

Distance from sun:	3.670 million miles	o
Diameter of planet:	About 2,000 miles	
Length of day:	Not known	Relative size in
Length of year:	248 years	comparison with
Satellites:	None	the other planets

Even after Neptune was discovered and its gravitational pull allowed for, Uranus still did not keep strictly to its predicted path, and astronomers began to suspect that yet another planet, out beyond Neptune, must be pulling that planet from its course. This time it was an American,

Dr. Percival Lowell, founder and director of the Lowell Observatory at Flagstaff, Arizona, who calculated how the supposed planet must move. After twenty-five years of search, and after his death, a planet was discovered, on January 21, 1930, by C. W. Tombaugh at Lowell Observatory, fairly near to where Lowell had predicted it should be. Public announcement was not made until March 13, the anniversary of the discovery of Uranus — which was also Lowell's birthday. The planet was named Pluto, after the god of the underworld. The symbol used for Pluto is made from the letters PL, the initials of Percival Lowell.

Pluto is so far away from the sun's heat, being forty times as far from the sun as we are, that most of the gases usually forming an atmosphere would be frozen solid. Its temperature is estimated at about 348 degrees below zero.

Pluto's orbit is elongated more than any other planet's. At its nearest approach to the sun, Pluto is less than 30 times as far away from the sun as is the earth. But when farthest from the sun Pluto is nearly 50 times as far away from the sun as is the earth. In 1989 Pluto's distance from the sun will actually be less than Neptune's, but Pluto and Neptune will not be very close to each other at that time. In the year 2178 Pluto will be again in the same point in its orbit where it was discovered. It has a long way to go for one circuit of its orbit and travels only one-eleventh as fast as Mercury.

Pluto is of the fifteenth magnitude and cannot be seen without using a large telescope. It is probably about one-quarter the size of the earth.

ASTEROIDS

Besides the nine planets there are thousands of smaller bodies, the largest only 250 miles across, traveling round and round the sun, most of them between Mars and Jupiter. Some astronomers believe them to be the shattered fragments of a single large planet, which may have once moved in the wide gap between the paths of Mars and Jupiter. Some of the asteroids come close to the earth. One called Eros comes within 13,000,000 miles from us, but is so small that it can only be seen in a large telescope.

COMETS

A comet may be the most awe-inspiring sight in the heavens, although many of them are visible only through a telescope or appear to the naked eye as small blurs of light. Comet means "hairy one." They fall in toward the sun from very far out in space, rush close past the sun, and swing back out whence they came. While near the sun they are made up of three parts: a magnificent "tail" sometimes as much as a hundred million miles long, made of gaseous material, which gives them their name; a bright ball-like head or "coma," also made of gas, and usually a bright starlike center of solid particles. This center is called a nucleus.

Comets do not have tails when they are at a great distance from the sun. Their gases are then all frozen. The light from the sun heats up, boils off, and exerts a pressure on these gases. As the comet approaches the sun, the pressure of the sunlight forces some of the gases out into a tail which alway points away from the sun whether the comet is approaching the sun or receding from

Yerkes Observatory

FIG. 76.—Halley's Comet, photographed May 4, 1910.

it. The farther a comet recedes from the sun, the shorter its tail becomes, until eventually the tail of the comet disappears entirely.

Comets move at great speeds in long, hairpin orbits around the sun, moving most rapidly when nearest the sun and slowest when farthest away. They spend most of the time far from our earth, and remain in our field of vision only a few weeks or months.

Since they are losing their material through their

FIG. 77.—Orbits of Halley's Comet and Comet of 1811. Dotted line shows orbit of Uranus.

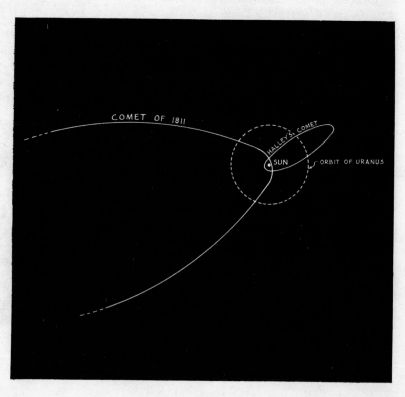

tails, comets cannot last very long, and astronomers believe that those that we see are not so old as our earth. They may have been pulled into our solar system from outside through the force of the sun's gravity, or they may be the remains of some recent explosion which has taken place within the solar system itself.

The more spectacular comets have always been regarded as portents of disaster by the superstitious. In the fifteenth century, when Halley's comet was in the sky, the prayer, "Lord, save us from the Devil, the Turk, and the Comet," was added to the service of European churches. Such dread of comets is groundless, and it has been calculated that the earth even passed through the outer part of that comet's tail in 1910. At the present time Halley's Comet is out beyond Neptune's orbit, traveling at a relatively slow speed. It turned back toward the sun in 1948 and should be visible again in 1985, since its period of revolution is 75 years. In 1986 it will pass around the sun, and once more it will start its long journey out into space.

Among the comets which have been observed more than once, none is known to have a period of revolution of as much as 100 years. The shortest known period for any comet is 3.3 years; this comet is only faintly visible to the naked eye. A number of comets which go out about as far as Jupiter's orbit, and are therefore known as Jupiter's family of comets, have a period of about 6 years. Since it takes Jupiter 12 years to revolve around the sun, can you think of one reason why this family' of comets takes only about half as long?

METEORS

If you have been looking at the constellation Perseus in early August, you may have been surprised to see a star apparently leave its place, dart across the sky, and quickly disappear. Yet when you looked again at the constellation you saw that all its stars were still in place. At other times of the year and in other parts of the sky, if you are in the country, far away from city lights, you will often see an occasional tiny speck of light start here or there among the stars, speed a short distance across the sky, and go out as suddenly as it appeared. You were seeing a meteor, commonly known as a shooting star. On most clear, moonless nights you cannot look at the sky for fifteen minutes without seeing at least one shooting star, and after midnight they are even more frequent. Periodically there are "meteor showers," when the numbers may be so great that the whole sky is bright. On such a night people who believe that a shooting star is a good omen would feel lucky indeed!

Of course no real star can appear to move so fast; they are huge suns very far away. These meteors, although they look like stars, are small bits of rock or iron, which burn up in our atmosphere some 70 or 80 miles above the earth. You can see more of them after midnight because then the air above you is on the front side of the earth in its motion around the sun, and we "run into" more meteors on the front side.

The meteors themselves are not at rest (some shoot in on the back side of the earth), and many of them are moving in groups, which account for the meteor showers. As-

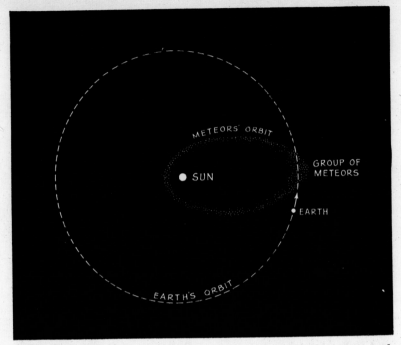

FIG. 78.—Diagram of the earth moving into a swarm of meteors such as produce a meteor shower.

tronomers have found that these groups of meteors follow long, thin orbits around the sun, like comets; in fact, these groups of small meteors are, most likely, old comets, spread out and no longer having any gas for a tail. Some of the meteors have separated from the main group and are spread along the orbit in a long belt around the sun. Each particle in a belt travels roughly the same path, so that the whole continuous belt, like a conveyor, travels ceaselessly around the sun, held to its path by the sun's gravity—just as our solid earth travels in a fixed path around the sun each year. The orbits or belts are not in the same plane, or level, as that followed by the earth and the other planets. Therefore, we are not surprised that the earth crosses several of these belts on its yearly journey around the sun.

As the earth sweeps along in its orbit it reaches at a given time each year the place where its path crosses such a meteor belt. The particles then come hurtling at us out of space and we are treated to the spectacle of a meteor shower. The meteoric particles as they travel their path around the sun are cold and dark, but as they move through the earth's atmosphere at enormous speed, tiny particles heated into white-hot sparks are stripped from them, much as sparks fly from a piece of iron held against a turning emery wheel. Most of the meteors are consumed before they get hot enough to shine directly. Those unusual pieces, perhaps nine or ten pounds in weight, which are large enough to have their surfaces heated to the point of incandescence, are called fireballs, and they look the part!

August is richer in meteors than any other month. Between August 9 and 12 each year the earth crosses a meteor belt. The shooting stars of this shower are known as the Perseid meteors, after the constellation Perseus. This does not mean that the stars of this constellation have anything to do with the swarms of shooting stars. Meteors, which are part of our solar system, have their beginning and their end so near our earth that they are far from the sphere of control of this distant constellation. The shower is given its name "Perseid" because if we were to prolong the arc of each of the shooting stars which we see during this period over all parts of the sky, they would all meet close to a single point which is in the heart of the constellation of Perseus. This point is known as the radiant of the shower. Actually the meteors do not emanate from the radiant and diverge as they travel, but are really coming toward us in parallel paths like the drops in a rainstorm. Their apparent diversion is an effect of perspective, caused by their great distance from us—in the same way that railroad tracks viewed from the rear platform of a train seem to converge in the distance, and the buildings on a long straight street appear to come together.

The Leonids, meteors with their radiant in the constellation of Leo, come around November 14 and 15, and may be best observed in the early morning hours. They are usually not in sufficient numbers to be spectacular. Showers coming from the region of Andromeda between November 23 and 27 are observable in the evening hours; showers from the vicinity of Lyra between April 19 and 21 may be observable all night. Around October 20 Orion furnishes the radiant for a shower, which is at its best after midnight. It must be kept in mind that these showers represent different bands of meteoric material, and that we pass through many more thin bands, which do not provide displays worthy of the name shower.

In some parts of the belts of meteoric particles the meteors are more thickly crowded together than in others. Since the orbits of the meteors are larger than the orbit of the earth, and since they travel at a different speed, we do not run into the same part of a belt each year. In the years when the earth dashes into a dense portion of a belt, the shower of meteors is unusually magnificent. The meteors in some streams are chiefly massed in a vast knot, and there are sometimes occasional gaps in the stream; this explains why some years bring no August display from the region of Perseus worthy of the name, while every 120 years the maximum display occurs. We were privileged to see this in 1932.

In 1833 the Leonid shower in November was so magnificent that many people thought the end of the world was upon them. On November 12 of that year the falling stars were as thick as snowflakes; many were as bright as the planet Venus, and their trails looked like the ribs of a giant umbrella. Generally this display is not at all brilliant, but once every 33 years it is of wonderful splendor, when the earth crosses a dense knot of meteoric material. The first recorded appearance of this shower was in 902, which was long known as the "Year of the Stars." The year 1932 was another "Year of the Stars." The next really magnificent display from this belt of meteors should come about 1965.

It is interesting to observe and count the meteors in such showers. The records have been used by astronomers in their search for new knowledge of the universe, of the unknown regions of our atmosphere 100 miles or more above the earth's surface, of comets, the northern lights, and other heavenly phenomena—as well as about the crust of the earth on which we walk. In the December, 1934, issue of *Popular Astronomy* is an article by Professor C. C. Wylie entitled, "How to Make Good Group Counts," which gives instructions for making observations that will be useful to scientists. Several groups of Boy Scouts and Girl Scouts have done this in summer camps.

The brightest meteors of the showers may be photographed by anyone with a fairly fast lens in his camera, say with a focal ratio of 4.5 or faster. If you have such a camera, set it on a firm support, pointing it toward the region where most of the shooting stars are appearing. Having it set for a time exposure, open the shutter and expose it for an hour at maximum aperture. If the sky is light from street lamps, twilight, or faint moonlight, the exposure should not be over half an hour, and should not be attempted if the moonlight is strong. To make a useful record write down the times of opening and closing the shutter, and a statement of the place where the exposures were made, exact enough to locate it on a map. The negatives, not prints, will be received gladly at the Harvard Observatory, Cambridge, Massachusetts, where experienced observers will search them for meteor trails.

The shower which occurs in the latter part of November, with its radiant in Andromeda, deserves special mention. The meteors pursue the same orbit around the sun as Biela's Comet, and it is probable that they are the products of its disintegration. The orbit of the August meteors is identical with that of a bright comet observed in 1862. The relation between comets and meteors is therefore intimate. A comet is a group of bodies and gas close together; a meteoric belt is a group of bodies more widely separated, and with little or no gas.

This quotation from Professor Wylie, of the University of Iowa, will help in distinguishing meteors from comets:

Because the general public often calls a bright meteor a comet, it is well to bring the more important distinctions together. . . . ,

135

as follows: The *light* of the comet is about that of a star, while the light of the spectacular meteor is about that of the Moon. The comet is *visible* for days or even months, while the meteor is visible for only a few seconds. The comet seems to remain *stationary* among the stars, while the meteor sweeps rapidly across the sky. The comet is a swarm of small and widely scattered particles, while the meteor is a single solid particle. The *volume* of the comet is greater than that of the Earth, while the meteor is no bigger than an ordinary ten-pound stone. The comet is millions of miles away, while the meteor is usually less than two hundred miles away, and always in the Earth's atmosphere.[1]

The average height of a shooting star when first seen has been found to be about 70 miles, and at about 55 miles above the earth it disappears. Since the average speed of a meteor is 25 miles per second the flash is very quick. Their size probably averages that of a grain of wheat.

Some of the brightest and largest meteors come as low as 5 to 25 miles above the earth's surface before bursting and disappearing. Fragments from them may fall to the surface of the earth as dark stones or pieces of iron, called meteorites, meaning "meteoric stone." Meteorites are usually stone and are made up of chemical elements well known on earth, but often combined in peculiar mineral forms. A few are largely of iron, the iron always combined with nickel. They show a network of crossing lines which is unlike that shown by iron smelted on earth. Meteorites are quite rare, and you very seldom see them except in a museum. There are many examples at the American Museum of Natural History in New York City, and the Chicago Museum of Natural History houses the

[1] Wylie, C. C., *Astronomy, Maps, and Weather.* (Harper & Bros.), p. 367.

world's greatest collection. You will notice that they are commonly covered with a crust like a thin layer of varnish, as if the outside had melted so suddenly that the heat had not gone far in, which is indeed the case.

Meteorites have been known to kill men and destroy buildings. Very few such catastrophes have been recorded, because buildings and men cover only a very small part of the earth, and meteorites are infrequent visitors. There are, however, hundreds of accounts of falls of meteorites during the past 2,500 years. The Greeks and Romans considered them as celestial omens and kept some of them in their temples. One at Mecca is adored by the Mohammedan faithful. An Ohio Indian mound has yielded copper earrings decorated with meteoric iron.

An interesting book on meteors and meteorites is *Our Stone-Pelted Planet* by H. H. Nininger, published by the Houghton Mifflin Company in 1933.

MOON

Average distance from earth:	238,857 miles
Diameter:	2,160 miles

As stargazers we could not have failed to notice the moon, and particularly so when its brightness all but prevented our study of the heavens. This may have led to the question: Why does the moon sometimes rise early, sometimes not until late in the evening, and why do we have a full moon, then again a half moon, and sometimes only a sliver of a new moon? First of all, we must remember that the moon revolves around the earth in a period of about 27 days. It is a sphere, and therefore the sun lights half of it, the half toward the sun, while the

137

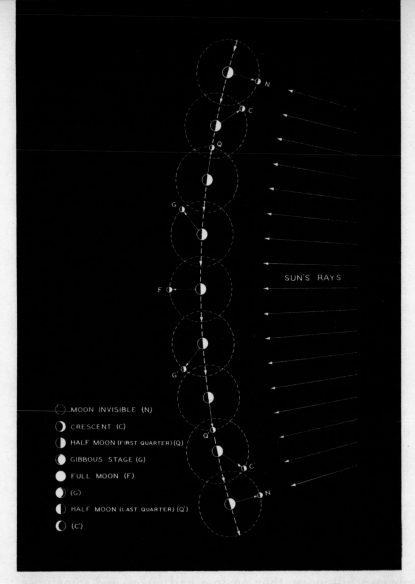

SUN'S RAYS

○ — MOON INVISIBLE (N)

◗ CRESCENT (C)

◗ HALF MOON (FIRST QUARTER) (Q)

◖ GIBBOUS STAGE (G)

● FULL MOON (F)

◗ (G')

◗ HALF MOON (LAST QUARTER) (Q')

◐ (C')

FIG. 79.—DIAGRAM TO EXPLAIN PHASES OF THE MOON. The moon is shown at eight different positions in its orbit around the earth. The earth is shown traveling in its path around the sun. Each arrow from the earth to the moon represents the line of sight from earth to moon. If you turn the book to look along any of these arrows and cover the half of the moon away from you, it will present the appearance shown in the key to the left, which shows successive phases of the moon.

other half remains in darkness. Like the planets the moon does not give out light of its own, but merely reflects the rays of light that it has received from the sun.

The diagram on page 138 is intended as an explanation of the phases of the moon. That body is shown at eight different positions in its orbit. The earth is shown meanwhile as it revolves about the sun. The sun's rays, represented as coming from the right, illuminate the right half of both earth and moon. When the moon is directly between us and the direction of the sun's rays, its dark side is toward us, and the moon is invisible. A few days later it has moved to such a position that we can see a small part of its bright surface, and we have a crescent moon. As the moon moves in its orbit, the crescent increases in size until, when it has reached first quarter, we see a half moon. After the gibbous stage we come to full moon, where the entire bright side is facing toward us so that we see the moon as a complete circle. Now the moon begins to wane, passing through these stages in reverse order, going from gibbous to last quarter (half moon), to crescent, and back to the "dark of the moon."

The earth, as seen from the moon, presents similar phases. At the time of the new moon, it has the appearance of a round, illuminated disk, and at full moon is invisible. When the moon is between us and the direction of the sun's rays, we can often notice that the part of the moon's face which is unilluminated by the sun, instead of being completely invisible, can be seen faintly because of the reflection on its dark surface of the light coming from the earth—actually secondhand light from the sun.

Fig. 80.—The earth-lit moon—"the old moon in the new moon's arms."

This is called "the old moon in the new moon's arms."

The moon does not rise at the same time every day. Not only that, but it does not always rise in the same part of the day, as does the sun! At new moon it comes over the horizon at about the same time as the sun and sets with it. But each day the moon rises on an average of about 50 minutes later than on the previous day, and at the end of the first quarter rises at midday and sets at midnight. Thus we often see the faint "half moon" in the afternoon sky when the sun is growing dim. When full the moon rises about sunset and sets at sunrise. At the beginning of the last quarter it rises at midnight and sets at midday. Thus the "half moon" is often seen in the morning sky.

Perhaps we can find an explanation of these phenomena in Figure 79. Each succeeding daily revolution of the earth on its axis gives us a continually changing view of the moon on its monthly journey around the earth. We notice from the diagram that the new moon and crescent phases are visible from the "day side" of the earth. A few days later we see the first quarter of the moon, when it is more in line with the "night side" of the earth. When the moon is in this phase, it appears to rise in the afternoon. The waxing gibbous phase of the moon is principally visible from the "night side." About two weeks after new moon, when the earth is between the sun and the moon, the full moon becomes visible at sunset and shines throughout the night. Still later we see the waxing gibbous phase, which is partly visible from the "day side." Finally, some morning almost two weeks after full moon,

141

the crescent moon rises with its horns to the west, being visible once more from the "day side."

Between the waning and the waxing crescents the moon disappears from sight (because it passes between the sun and the earth) and reappears on the other (or east) side of the sun. The horns of the waning moon appear to point to the west, while those of the waxing moon point to the east. In both cases the horns are actually turned away from the sun. When the horns are pointing toward the east, the sun has just set in the west; when the horns are pointing to the west, the sun is about to rise in the east.

Knowing now the cause of the phases of the moon, we can realize how groundless are the superstitions which have grown up about it. There is a weather proverb which tells us that when the horns of the moon tip up, it is holding rain from the earth, and we shall have dry weather. When the horns tip down toward the earth they will spill the water, and we shall have a rainy season. Of course these two conditions are reached in the natural revolution of the moon about our planet, and could have no effect on our weather! The moon could not possibly affect the "luck" of growing plants on the earth, as is hinted in the adage that potatoes will "go to tops" *unless* planted in the dark of the moon, or, in another version, *if* planted in the dark of the moon. Even the very tellers of the adage cannot seem to decide which way it is! In fact, the only true moon proverb is, "A ring around the moon is a sign of rain." However, the moon has nothing to do with bringing the rain. The ring is caused by cloud particles in our atmosphere which reflect the moonbeams and make a halolike circle of light. Since certain types of misty clouds foretell rain, the proverb is often true.

The phenomenon of the tides is practically the only noticeable effect of the moon on the earth. Tides are the daily rising and falling of the waters of the ocean. They are caused by the gravitational pull of the sun and the moon upon the earth. The moon, being so much nearer us than the sun, is the more important tide-producing agent.

There are two "low tides"—and also two "high tides" —about every twenty-four hours and fifty minutes. Beginning at low tide, there is a gradual rise for about six hours until high tide, when the water remains stationary for a short time. Then it begins to recede and continues to fall for the next six hours, gradually coming to its former low mark on the beach. The highest stage is called high tide, and the lowest ebb tide. These terms have been applied to the water heights as observed on ocean shores, for it is difficult to distinguish tides on the open sea. On inland lakes and rivers the tides are too small to be observed.

In Figure 81, the line drawn through *ACB* is a diameter of the earth in line with the direction of the moon at a certain time. Since *A* is nearer the moon than *C*, the moon will attract it more strongly, and likewise *C* will be attracted more strongly than *B*. Thus the diameter *ACB* tends to be lengthened, and in effect *A* and *B* would each be moved farther from *C*. The solid portion of the earth

143

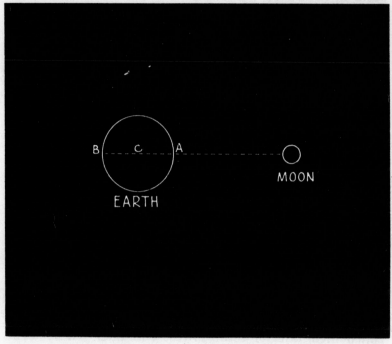

Fig. 81.—Diagram to illustrate the cause of tides.

is very rigid, about as rigid as steel, so it does not yield appreciably to these forces. If this were not so, the earth as a whole would be continuously deformed, like a soft rubber ball pulled by a suction cup. As it is, the effect of the moon's gravitational pull is felt chiefly by the waters on the earth's surface. The effect of the tidal forces is to move the waters of the ocean into two bulges, at A and B. We thus have high tides at two places on the earth at once, near A and B, and low tides at two places in between. In a little more than 12 hours, when the earth has turned its other side toward the moon, high tides again

144

occur at *A* and *B*. (The drag of the rotating earth on the water of the seas carries these bulges eastward, so that tides are actually later than expected.)

The sun's effect in producing tides is a little less than half that of the moon. When the moon is new (moon between sun and earth) or full (earth between moon and sun), the tide-raising forces of the moon and sun act together — since all three are approximately in the same straight line. The high tides are then higher and the low tides lower and are known as *spring* tides. During the first and last quarters of the moon, the sun and moon are not pulling together, but practically at right angles to each other. The effect of this is to make the high tides lower and the low tides higher; these tides are called *neap* tides.

You will probably find it interesting to look at a tide table, such as that of New York City in *The World Almanac*. Notice especially the varying times between tides throughout the year. They correspond roughly to the time the moon seems to lag behind from night to night.

The moon also plays a leading part in one of nature's most magnificent spectacles, an eclipse of the sun. The diameter of the sun is about four hundred times that of the moon, but, since the sun is almost four hundred times as far away, the two bodies appear of approximately the same size in the sky. An eclipse of the sun occurs when the moon is in a direct line between the earth and the sun. The figure below shows the cause of an eclipse. The moon's tapering shadow falls on the earth at the area marked

145

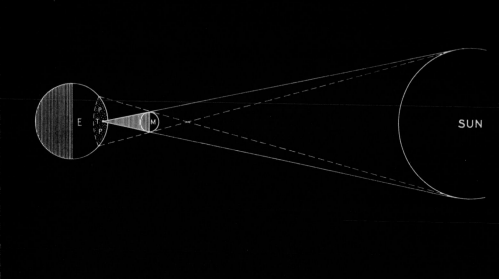

Fig. 82.—Conditions causing an eclipse of the sun.

T, where observers would see a total eclipse of the sun, its disk completely hidden behind that of the moon. From the area indicated by the light shading, *P*, the observers would see only a partial eclipse, for the sun would only be partly hidden. As the moon revolves about the earth, the small black shadow, *T*, and the larger gray shadow, *P*, move across the earth's surface. This explains maps of the time and the regions where eclipses may be seen, the "path of totality," *T*, shown as a black band. Under the most favorable conditions, the width of this belt is 168 miles, and the duration of total eclipse almost eight minutes. Usually, however, the belt is less than 100 miles wide and the duration of the eclipse about two minutes.

The conditions that cause an eclipse of the moon are shown in the figure below. The earth's shadow is long and tapering, stretching away from the sun. When the moon crosses this shadow it is said to be eclipsed. The earth blots out the sun's rays, but some of them are bent in passing through the earth's atmosphere and so illuminate the moon, making it faintly visible. It takes on a rather weird copper tint. To understand the presence of this hue we must remember that white light like that given off by the sun contains all colors of light mixed in such proportions that the result is white. As the sunlight comes to the moon through the atmosphere which surrounds our planet, most of the blue light is absorbed, making that which reaches the moon and is reflected from it a coppery color.

The moon in its course passes between the earth and the sun once every month. Once each month also the moon passes us on the other side so that the earth is between the moon and the sun. Therefore we at first may wonder why there is not an eclipse of the sun and one of

Fig. 83.—Conditions causing an eclipse of the moon.

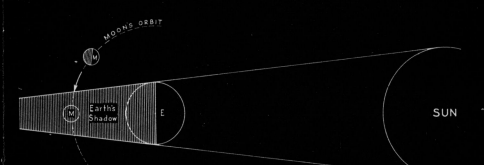

the moon every month. The reason is that the orbit of the moon is not in the same plane as that of the sun, and so the moon does not usually pass directly between earth and sun, but may be as much as five degrees above the sun or five degrees below it. This prevents the frequent occurrence of eclipses. However, both lunar and solar eclipses occur on a definite schedule. Each year there are from two to five solar eclipses, which are usually not total eclipses as viewed from any part of the earth. Periodically there is a total eclipse visible from a limited district. Each of these solar eclipses is repeated after an interval called the *saros*, about eighteen years and eleven days. The following is a list of the dates of the next four total eclipses of the sun visible in any part of the United States, together with the states in which they will be visible: June 30, 1954, Minnesota and Wisconsin; October 2, 1959, Massachusetts; July 20, 1963, Maine; and March 7, 1970, Florida, Georgia, and the Carolinas. The first two come just after sunrise, but the last two occur in the afternoon when conditions for viewing them are better. In the United States there will not be a total eclipse of the sun visible all the way across the country until 2017. Lunar eclipses are rarer, never more than three occurring in a year, and sometimes there are none. However, a total eclipse of the moon is always visible over at least a half of the earth's surface.

Everyone has heard of the "man in the moon." Through a field glass or opera glass, the markings, which to the unaided eye make up his features, resolve themselves into vast plains and mountain ranges. The most striking feature on the surface of the moon, as viewed through a small telescope, is the abundance of craters — circular depressions — some at least fifty miles in diameter with walls 20,000 feet high, others not more than a quarter mile across. The origin of these craters on the moon is a debated question among astronomers. Some say that they were caused by huge meteors which crashed into the moon, others that they are the result of volcanic explosions. We have never seen much more than half of the surface of the moon, since it always keeps the same side turned towards us. This is because one rotation of the moon is made in the same length of time as one trip around our planet.

The only important source of heat and light for both the earth and the moon is the sun. Energy from the sun reaches us in the form of radiations of comparatively short wave length, some of them visible as light. Most of them come straight through our atmosphere to the earth's surface, where they are absorbed and turned into heat. (Fortunately for us, some of the radiations of the shortest wave lengths—too much of which would be harmful to life here on earth—are absorbed high in our atmosphere.) The warmed earth then radiates this energy back into the atmosphere. But now it is in the form of long-wavelength heat radiations which can be readily absorbed by the carbon dioxide and water vapor in the atmosphere. This absorption prevents the surface of the earth from becoming unbearably hot while the sun is shining on it.

Then, too, the ability of the atmosphere to absorb and hold the earth's radiated heat prevents a rapid escape of heat by night. Because of this we avoid extremes in temperature by day and by night, and between summer and winter. Without it we should be exposed to terrible vicissitudes of cold and heat.

The moon has no atmosphere and no water. (The "seas" on the moon are not water, but only large, dark, smooth areas where craters are not numerous. Through the low-power telescopes used by Galileo, their first observer, they looked like seas, and were called *maria*.) Although each square mile of the two bodies receives about equal quantities of heat from the sun, the moon, without a protecting atmosphere, becomes enormously hot during its period of daylight. Its surface temperature rises to as much as 214 degrees, a little higher than that of boiling water. After two weeks of this intense heat, as the long lunar day ends, the temperature sinks quickly to about 250 degrees below zero, as the heated side of the moon is turned away from the sun. For there is no blanket of atmosphere to hold the heat. With these extremes of temperature, and the absence of air and water, it is hardly necessary to state that no life of any type that we know could exist on the moon.

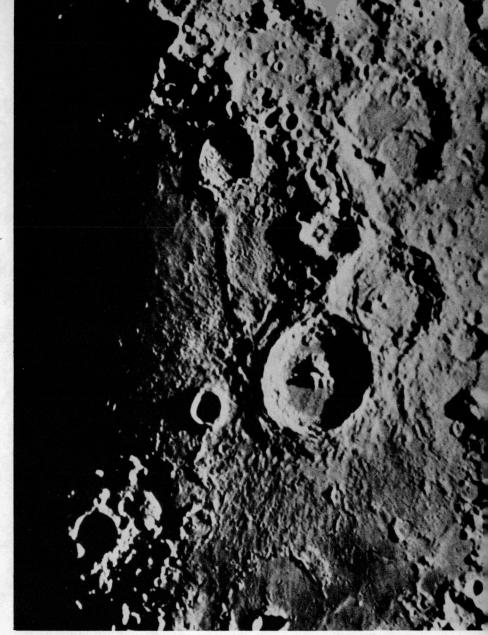

FIG. 84.—The lunar crater Theophilus.

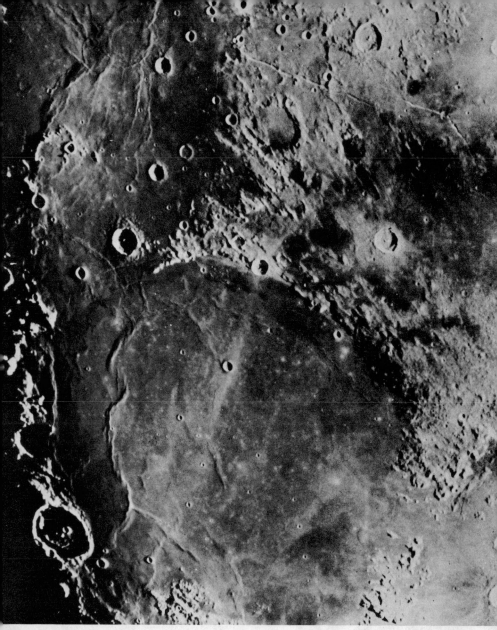

FIG. 85.—Lunar "seas": Mare Serenitatis (Sea of Serenity) and Mare Tranquilitatis (Sea of Tranquillity).

152

SUN

Average distance from earth: 93,003,000 miles
Diameter: 864,000 miles

The sun's distance from the earth varies from 91,300,000 miles in January to 94,500,000 miles in July. Its average distance from the earth is generally called 93,000,000 miles in round numbers. As a result of nine years of co-operation by 45 observatories located throughout the world, the accurate figure for the sun's average distance from the earth, given at the beginning of this section, has been determined. Many problems in astronomy are being investigated in this co-operative way.

Though the sun is only one of millions of stars, and not even one of the largest, it is, to us on earth, by far the most important object in the universe. We are dependent on it for heat and light. No form of life could exist on our planet were its influence withdrawn.

We all know that the changing temperatures of the various seasons are due to the sun, but most of us do not realize that the sun is actually about three million miles nearer the earth in our winter than it is in our summer. The rays of the sun, however, do not strike us from the same angle in the different seasons. Perhaps you have noticed that in summer the sun at midday is almost overhead, but in winter it is far to the south. An explanation of this phenomenon is shown in Figure 86. In order to understand it, we must remember that the earth's axis is inclined by 66½ degrees to the plane of its orbit. Point *a* marks the approximate latitude of Chicago. A line drawn

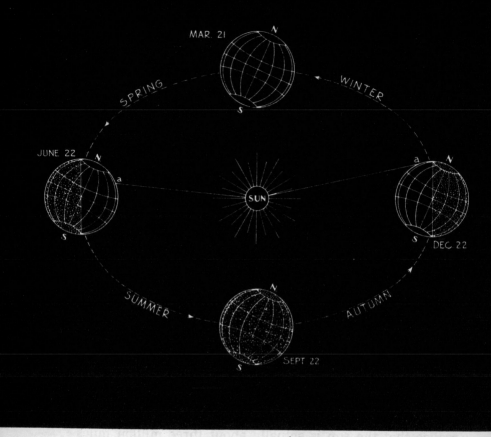

Fig. 86.—Causes of the seasons.

from the sun to point *a* on June 22 will meet the surface at nearly a right angle, while a similar line drawn to the same point on December 22 will make a very acute angle with the surface.

But why should there be a difference in the heat whether the sun's rays come to us at a right angle and the sun is high in the heavens, or whether the rays come from the southern sky and strike us at an acute angle?

154

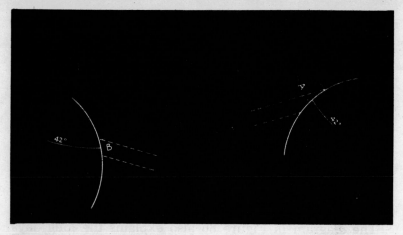

FIG. 87.—*A* shows area covered by a ray of light from the sun as it strikes the earth on December 22. Compare with *B*, the area covered by a ray of like size as it strikes the earth on June 22.

In Figure 87, *A* represents the area covered by a ray of sunlight as it strikes the earth on December 22 at an acute angle; *B*, the smaller area covered by a ray of like size as it strikes the earth on June 22. Naturally a ray spread over a large area will not heat any part of that area as much as one which must spread its heat over only a small portion. Can you explain why the Southern Hemisphere enjoys summer while it is winter here, and vice versa? A moment's study of the diagram of the seasons shows why the equatorial regions and the tropics have year-round heat. The sun's rays meet these parts at almost a right angle at all seasons of the year. It will also be seen that the sun's rays always strike the extreme northern and southern regions at an acute angle, thus accounting for their year-round coldness.

Figure 86 also explains the seasonal changes in the length of day and night. We can see that in winter the

155

area at *a* has only a short distance to rotate before it passes into the region not reached by the sun's rays. In other words, the winter days are short. In summer, however, the area *a* can rotate for a much longer time before passing into the region of darkness, and so summer days are longer than winter days. At the equator all days are of the same length.

The angle of the sun's rays and the number of hours during which it shines work together to make the earth and air warmer in summer than in winter.

The diagram in Figure 86 also explains the long days and nights of the polar regions. Look at it and you will see why on June 22 the entire area inside the Arctic Circle is enjoying daylight and why on that date the sun does not set anywhere within the Arctic Circle during the entire 24-hour day. As we go north from the Arctic Circle the summer period of continuous daylight lasts longer and longer; for, if you will look at the diagram and imagine the earth moving along in its path around the sun, you will see that the farther north an area is located, the greater the number of days it will stay within the zone of light during its daily rotation. On June 22, the long summer "day," six months long at the North Pole, is about half over. At the same time the corresponding areas of the Antarctic are halfway through their long siege of cold winter night. On December 22, the north polar region is halfway through its long winter night, while the south polar regions are enjoying varying amounts of continuous daylight in their turn.

All that can be seen of the sun by an observer on the

earth is its shining surface. This is known to astronomers as the *photosphere*. Outside the photosphere is an envelope of less dense gas, the *chromosphere*. Its resemblance to a great blazing fire led one astronomer to describe it as a "prairie in flames." (Actually it is too hot on the sun for anything to burn, as we use the term.) The nature of the material behind the photosphere and chromosphere is a matter for conjecture. Through telescopes we can frequently see red flamelike tongues of hot gas spurting from the chromosphere, so huge that beside them our earth would be a speck. Sometimes their height is great enough to equal a distance double that of the moon from the earth. These outbursts of gas come with the fury of a volcanic eruption. Beyond the chromosphere, the sun is surrounded by an envelope called the *corona*. Only at the time of total eclipse, when the brilliant disk of the sun is obscured by the moon, can the solar corona be studied. For this reason astronomers often travel half-

Fig. 88.—Total eclipse of the sun, showing solar corona.

Yerkes Observatory

way around the earth to view an eclipse. The inner part of the corona is intensely bright and tapers into an outer portion of soft light, with streamers spreading millions of miles into space. It appears as a halo of pearly light. The temperature of the sun is so great that in its atmosphere we find the metals vaporized. While our atmosphere consists mainly of oxygen and nitrogen, that of the sun is made up of gaseous iron, lead, zinc, etc., as well as the elements common in our atmosphere.

The surface of the sun is often dotted with dark irregularly shaped patches, some of which are as large as 60,000 miles in diameter. Others as small as 100 miles in diameter have been seen through telescopes, and undoubtedly these are not the smallest. These patches are known as *sunspots* and are dark only in comparison with the brightness of the sun. The sun's surface temperature is about 11,000 degrees, and the sunspots are close to 7,000 degrees. We hear frequently that sunspots have their effect on earth conditions. Scientists are convinced that the spots are connected with storms on the sun. When the spots are most numerous we have magnetic "storms," which cause trouble with telegraph and telephone connections and radio reception. A more pleasant result of these magnetic storms is the phenomenon of the northern lights which we see in the heavens. The connection between sunspots and weather is less definite. However, many scientists believe that the temperature of our atmosphere is lower when sunspots are most numerous. There is some evidence of a connection between sunspots and rainfall, but unfortunately this evidence is rather vague at the present time. The sunspots reach their maximum

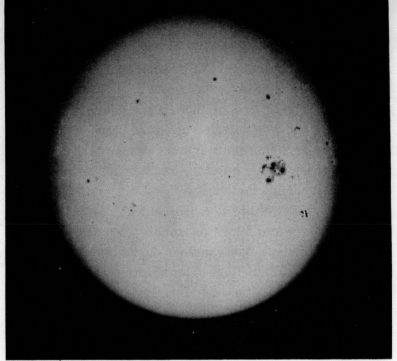

FIG. 89.—Direct photograph of sun's disk, showing large and small spots.

number every eleven years, and they seem to come in fairly regular cycles.

Like the earth, the sun is turning on its axis. It does not turn like a solid body. On the earth, all latitudes rotate in the same period. Sitka, Chicago, Bogotá, all complete their rotation in twenty-four hours. But spots on the sun's equator make their circuit more quickly than spots at higher latitudes. The region around the equator rotates in about 24½ days, while points within 10 degrees of the poles take about 35 days to complete a rotation. The rotation period at the poles would be still greater, but has not yet been determined.

Why is it that the sun does not cool down and cease to

give out light and heat? Year after year, century after century, eon after eon, it has shed life-giving warmth on the earth. The record of more than a billion years of continuous sunshine is sealed up in the rocks of the earth. Where does this enormous amount of energy come from? If we can answer this question for the sun, we shall have answered it for all the stars.

The old theory that the sun is burning and giving out heat cannot account for it. It would have consumed itself ages ago. We must have another explanation. You have heard of chemical reactions in which atoms of one element unite with atoms of another element to produce a new substance, in such changes as the rusting of iron. Here the quantity of matter is not changed, for the exact amount of oxygen taken from the air is present in the rust compound. Now it has been discovered that there are also changes of an entirely different sort: that some elements, by rearrangements within the atom, may go through a process of change into other elements. Radium changes of itself into helium, lead, and various other elements, and chemists have actually succeeded in artificially changing one element to another in a limited way. Such subatomic changes produce energy, for in the transformation of one element to another, a small amount of matter constantly is wasted, or changed from matter into energy. It is such changes within the atom that are believed to produce the greater part of the sun's energy. While they are most rare on earth, it is thought that in the enormous temperatures of the interior of the sun — estimated to be as high as 40,000,000 degrees — they are common. The chief such action thought to account for the energy of the sun is the conversion of hydrogen atoms to helium atoms. In this change, astronomers have calculated that about one per cent of the hydrogen involved is converted into short-wave radiation. Since a large per cent of the sun's mass is hydrogen, this short-wave radiation — the source of our light and heat — amounts to an enormous quantity, sufficient to supply radiation during the estimated age of the sun — 5,000,000,000 years — and for many billions of years to come.

If you are interested in these changes and in the world of atoms, you may wish to read the section called "The Microscopic Universe," in the book, *Planets, Stars, and Atoms,* by George E. Frost.

There have been many theories as to the origin of the solar system. One favored by many astronomers tells us

Fig. 90.—Diagram to illustrate the Chamberlin-Moulton theory of the origin of the earth. As shown in *A*, another star is thought to have rushed past, narrowly missing the sun; gases were pulled out from both the sun and the other star by their gravitational forces. Later, as shown in *B*, these gases condensed to form a vast number of meteor-like bodies, the larger of which grew by sweeping up the smaller ones, later to form the planets. Under this theory, the intruding star would also have had planets form.

Drawn by Sol Ehrlich for Physics Today

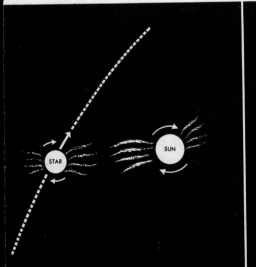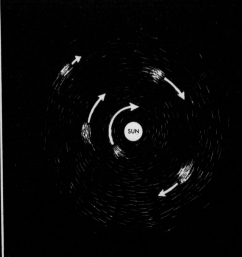

that the planets were made of material erupted from the sun, and were started on their orbits by the gravitational force of a passing star, a force great enough, as the star passed close to the sun, to overcome that body's gravity. This theory, proposed by two University of Chicago scientists, T. C. Chamberlin, a geologist, and F. R. Moulton, an astronomer, in 1900, may be found, in understandable fashion, in *The Solar System and Its Origin* by H. N. Russell, published in 1935 by the Macmillan Company.

More recently an early theory of the German philosopher, Immanuel Kant, has been revised by Professor Weizsäcker in Germany and Professor Kuiper at the Yerkes Observatory. According to this theory no other star was involved; the planets and sun condensed out of a large rotating cloud of gas and meteors. One interesting consequence of this theory is that other suns—many of the stars we can see in the sky—may have planets moving around them, although we have no means of seeing such planets with present telescopes.

TELLING TIME

So regularly do all the stars appear to move in their courses that the exact measurement of time is the business of the astronomer. It is he who keeps our clocks correctly set. In the early days of civilization, the day lasted from sunrise to sunset and was divided into a definite number of hours. However, as the seasons change, the length of the daylight varies, so that throughout the year there is no uniformity either in the length of the hour or in the time by this method. The passing of larger intervals of time was marked by the moon's phases. A "moon" was the length of time it took that body to run through its phases: new moon, crescent, half moon, full moon, and back again. The "moons" were of regular lengths, but there were only arbitrary ways of grouping them to form longer intervals of time. Later, the counting of six moons for summer and six for winter made a period coinciding roughly with the year as we know it.

Exact time may be measured by the apparent motion of the stars. In order to understand this, we must study the celestial sphere. The sky is that part of the celestial sphere which is visible at any given time. We have learned that the North Pole of the earth points to the north pole of the celestial sphere; and that the South Pole of the earth points to the south pole of the celestial sphere. The earth's equator may be prolonged to cut the celestial sphere in a similar "celestial equator." We know that a meridian on the earth's surface is a semicircle passing from the North Pole to the South Pole. Such a line may be drawn through any place on earth. On a globe of the earth you will see these lines drawn in at equal intervals. Corresponding to these terrestrial meridians are the celestial meridians which pass from the north celestial pole to the south celestial pole. All these imaginary lines in the sky are illustrated in Figure 91.

The *ecliptic* is the apparent yearly path of the sun in the sky. To an observer on earth, the sun seems to be traveling around a hollow sphere, daily appearing on the eastern horizon in the morning and disappearing in the west at night. Also, the sun appears to be making a complete revolution through the sky during the course of a year, coming around at the end of twelve months to the place among the stars that it occupied at the beginning.

As we have learned, these apparent daily and yearly journeys of the sun are caused by the actual movements of the earth. The rotation of the earth on its axis every twenty-four hours from west to east causes the whole sky (sun and stars) to appear to rotate daily from east to west, and the yearly revolution of the earth around the sun makes it appear to us as if the sun were moving among the stars from west to east.

We must also define the *vernal equinox*. In winter the sun appears south of the celestial equator, and in summer north of it. Therefore, between these seasons, it apparently crosses the equator. The point at which it

Fig. 91.—The celestial sphere drawn in three dimensions. Note Vernal Equinox *(VE)* and Autumnal Equinox *(AE)* where the ecliptic (yearly path of the sun) crosses the celestial equator. Dot on *E* (Earth) shows position of observer. Fine dotted lines show the celestial meridians.

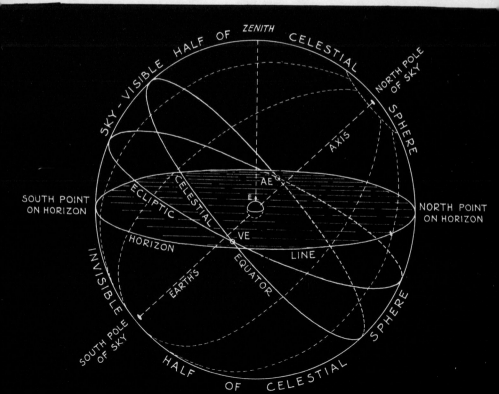

crosses the equator, going north, is known as the vernal
equinox; and going south, the autumnal equinox. (The
vernal equinox is used in determining the date on which
Easter falls, since Easter comes on the first Sunday after
the first full moon after the sun passes the vernal
equinox.)

Knowing these facts we may go on to a definition of a
sidereal day. It is defined as the interval of time between
successive passages of any meridian across the vernal
equinox, as the earth rotates. Also, the sidereal day may
be defined as the time interval between two successive
passages of a star across a given meridian. The sidereal
year is the time interval required for the sun apparently
to move from any position with respect to the stars, as seen
from the earth, around to the same position again.

True solar time is the time defined by the rotation of
the earth with reference to the sun. A solar day is the
interval between two successive passages of a meridian
across the center of the sun. However, in its apparent
annual motion, the sun seems to move eastward among
the stars, and so the solar day is, on the average, nearly
four minutes longer than a sidereal day. Do you remember reading on page 7 that each night the Big Dipper
reaches a given position about 4 minutes earlier than it
did the night before? The sun appears to make a circuit
of 360 degrees in 365.2422 days, and it therefore moves
eastward with respect to the stars about 1 degree per day.

But if we try to set our watches or clocks by the sun,
we find that it is not a reliable timekeeper. At different
times of the year it varies from about a quarter of an
hour too slow to about a quarter of an hour too fast. One

of the reasons for the sun's being apparently slow or fast is that the earth, in its revolution around the sun each year, does not always travel at the same speed. Since the motion of the earth around the sun is not uniform, with the result that the solar days are not of equal length, astronomers have taken the average of all the solar days in a year and called it the *mean* (or average) *solar day*.

Mean solar time is the time in ordinary use. The mean solar day is divided into 24 mean solar hours, these in turn into 60 mean solar minutes, and these again into 60 mean solar seconds each. The year consists of 365.2422 mean solar days, and is defined as the time it takes for the sun apparently to move from an equinox — the vernal equinox, for instance — back to the same equinox.

This year is also called a *tropical* year by astronomers. As you know, once during the year the sun's rays are perpendicular at the Tropic of Cancer; six months later they are perpendicular at the Tropic of Capricorn. The tropical year is the time required for the sun to move from either tropic back to the *same* tropic again. It contains one more sidereal day than it does mean solar days.

There is one more year for us to consider — the *calendar* year, also called the *civil* or *legal* year. It is the year with which the calendar is supposed to agree, although it gave the calendar makers plenty of trouble in the past. Under the old Julian calendar of 365¼ days to a year, an entire day was gained in about 128 years, because the calendar year was about 11 minutes longer than the tropical year. At the time the Gregorian calendar was adopted, this difference, which amounted at that time to 10 days, had become quite noticeable. Midwinter (the time of the shortest day) was occurring about December 12 instead of about December 22. So these 10 days were dropped, and October 5, 1585, became October 15. Then in order to keep the calendar from gaining again, only 97 leap years were to be added every 400 years; this was to be done by not adding leap years in the century years not divisible by 400. This change made the average calendar year only .0003 of a mean solar day (about 26 seconds) longer than a tropical year.

According to mean solar or sun time, when the sun is on the meridian at a given place, it is noon there. However, as the earth turns on its axis from west to east, the sun appears to travel from east to west. The point where the sun is on the meridian is also moving from east to west. Thus, the sun is on the meridian in Chicago an hour later than it is in New York City. So, when it is noon by sun time in New York, it is only 11 o'clock in Chicago. East of New York it is afternoon, because the sun has already seemed to pass the meridian there. Every fraction of a degree of longitude has a different true noon. (And therefore a different two o'clock, and three o'clock, and four o'clock, etc.) Naturally, when this sun time was used, it led to great confusion. It was especially annoying to travelers, for each city and town had its own brand of time (incidentally, this is the time registered by sundials), and each railroad went by that of the city where it had its headquarters. Because of this confusion, in 1883, our present system of standard time was introduced. All calculations involved in standard time are based on the time of the meridian which passes through Greenwich, England. When it is noon there, it is midnight exactly

180 degrees — halfway round the world — from there, east or west. For every 15 degrees east or west of Greenwich the time is an hour later or earlier, since this is the distance that the sun appears to travel in an hour. If we remember that the sun appears to travel 360 degrees, around the world, in 24 hours, this statement will be clear. The meridians at even 15-degree intervals from Greenwich in the United States are those 75, 90, 105, and 120 degrees west of Greenwich. The time on each of these meridians is extended through a zone of about 7 or 8 degrees east and west of each of these meridians, making four time zones, each roughly 15 degrees wide, and each central meridian located just 15 degrees from the next one. The 75th meridian determines Eastern standard time, five hours earlier by the clock than Greenwich time; the 90th meridian, Central standard time, six hours earlier; Mountain time is determined by the 105th meridian, seven hours earlier; and Pacific time is determined by the 120th meridian, eight hours earlier than Greenwich time.

We have seen from the above that we are one hour earlier than Greenwich time each fifteen degrees that we go west from Greenwich. When we have gone 360 degrees west and are back again at Greenwich, we have gained 24 hours. To avoid the paradox of having both yesterday and today at Greenwich at the same time, the International Date Line has been established near the 180th meridian (marked on most globes of the world), where an old day is always ending and a new day beginning. The old day is on the east side, and the new day on the west. Ships sailing westward lose a day as they cross this line. Ships sailing eastward gain a day.

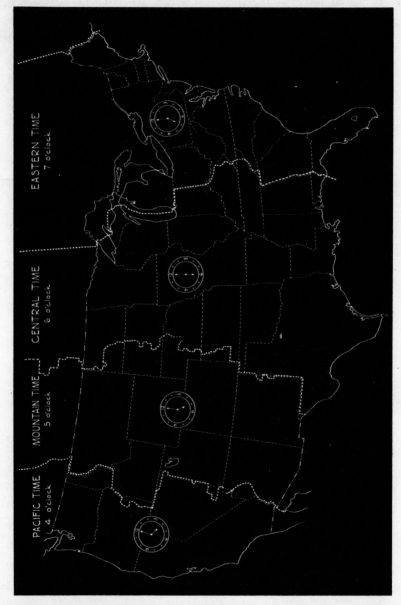

Fig. 92.—The four time belts of the United States.

9. Introduction to the Guides

If you would like to become familiar with more constellations, or would like to be sure of exactly where to find a star group at a certain hour and date, you will like sky charts. One of the most useful is *The Handy Star Finder*. Two excellent and clear books, with twelve maps for different dates and hours, are *Guide to the Constellations* and *Pathfinder Star Maps*. Another good set of maps of the skies may be found in McKready's *A Beginner's Star-Book*. Maps of individual constellations with directions for locating each, and a history and explanation of the division of the sky into constellations may be found in *How to Identify the Stars*.

If you liked the legends best, if you want to know more about man's view of the stars when they were looked on as jewels embedded in a solid sky, you will be interested in *Stars Through Magic Casements*, and *The Romance of Astronomy*.

If it is the wonder and mystery of the stars, the desire to know more about the universe that holds you, you will want to read such books as *Man and the Stars*, *Stars and Planets*, and "The Harvard Books on Astronomy," marked with an asterisk (*) in the book list which follows.

And so, good luck to you in your own explorations of the heavens, and in your further reading about those discoveries which have helped man to solve so many of the riddles of the universe!

SUGGESTED READING

Astronomy. By Forest Ray Moulton. The Macmillan Company, New York, 1916.

Astronomy. By William T. Skilling and Robert S. Richardson. Henry Holt and Company, New York, 1947.

Astronomy, Maps, and Weather. By C. C. Wylie. Harper & Brothers, New York, 1942.

*Atoms, Stars and Nebulae. By Leo Goldberg and Lawrence Aller. The Blakiston Company, Philadelphia, 1943.

Beginner's Star-Book, A. By Kelvin McKready (Edgar Gardner Murphy). G. P. Putnam's Sons, New York, 1924.

*Between the Planets. By Fletcher G. Watson. The Blakiston Company, Philadelphia, 1941.

*Earth, Moon and Planets. By Fred L. Whipple. The Blakiston Company, Philadelphia, 1941.

Field Book of the Skies. By William T. Olcott and Edmund W. Putnam. G. P. Putnam's Sons, New York, 1929.

*Galaxies. By Harlow Shapley. The Blakiston Company, Philadelphia, 1943.

Guide to the Constellations. By Samuel G. Barton and W. H. Barton. McGraw-Hill Book Company, New York, 1943.

Handy Star Finder, The. Published by C. S. Hammond & Company, Brooklyn, New York, 1948.

How to Identify the Stars. By Willis I. Milham. The Macmillan Company, New York, 1909.

Let's Look at the Stars. By Edwin B. Frost. Houghton Mifflin Company, Boston, 1935.

Man and the Stars. By Harlan T. Stetson. McGraw-Hill Book Company, New York, 1930.

*Milky Way, The. By Bart J. Bok and Priscilla F. Bok. The Blakiston Company, Philadelphia, 1941.

*Our Sun. By Donald H. Menzel. The Blakiston Company, Philadelphia, 1949.

Pathfinder Star Maps. By Edward S. King. The Cosmos Press, Inc., Cambridge, Mass., 1926.

Planets, Stars, and Atoms. By George E. Frost. The Caxton Printers, Ltd., Caldwell, Idaho, 1939.

Romance of Astronomy, The. By Florence Armstrong Grondal. The Macmillan Company, New York, 1941.

Stars and Planets. By Donald H. Menzel. The University Society, Inc., New York, 1931.

Stars Through Magic Casements. By Julia Williamson. D. Appleton-Century Company, New York, 1930.

Stars To-night. By Sara Teasdale. The Macmillan Company, New York, 1930.

*Story of the Variable Stars, The. By Leon Campbell and Luigi Jacchia. The Blakiston Company, Philadelphia, 1941.

*Telescopes. By George Z. Dimitroff and James G. Baker. Doubleday & Company, New York, 1945.

Index and Pronouncing Guide

In cases where authorities differ on the pronunciation of astronomical names, the recommendations adopted by the American Astronomical Society in 1942 have been followed.

KEY TO PRONUNCIATION

ABBREVIATIONS
d. drawing   *p.* photograph

173

174

Clock: Big Dipper as, 6-7; moons of Jupiter as, 118

Clusters. *See* Star clusters

Colors of stars: first-magnitude, 101; indication of stage of development, 73-74; relation to temperature, 72

Comets: 126, 128, 135-36; *p.* 127; Biela's, 135; brightness, 109, 136; distance, 136; distinguished from meteors, 135-36; Halley's, 129; *d.* 128; *p.* 127; Jupiter's family of, 129; meaning of name, 126; orbits, 126, 128, 129; origin, 129; parts, 126, 128, 135, 136; portents of disaster, 129; size, 136

Conon (kō'non), 66

Constellations. *See* Andromeda; Aquila; Auriga; Berenice's Hair; Big Dipper; Big Dog; Boötes; Cassiopeia; Cepheus; Cygnus; Draco; Gemini; Hercules; Job's Coffin; Leo; Little Dipper; Lyra; Manger; Northern Crown; Orion; Pegasus; Perseus; Pleiades; Sagittarius; Scorpius; Southern Fish; Taurus; Virgo

Constellations, groups of: Royal Family of the Sky, 31; *d.* 37; Summer Triangle, 50-51, 99; *d.* 51, 59

Copernicus (kô-pûr'nĭ-kûs), 105

Corona, solar, 157-58; *p.* 157

Corona Borealis (kô-rō'nå bō'rĕ-ā'lĭs). *See* Northern Crown

Crab. *See* Cancer

Cygnus (sĭg'nûs) the Swan: appearance, 57; *d.* 55, 59; legend, 56; location, 53, 57; *d.* 59; radio-broadcasting region in, 57-58

Dante (dän'tĕ), 45

Deimos (dī'mŏs), 114

Delphinus (dĕl-fī'nûs). *See* Job's Coffin

Delta Cephei (dĕl'tå sē'fĕ-ī), 41; *d.* 35

Deneb (dĕn'ĕb): brightness, 50, 57, 101; color, 101; distance, 101; location, 50, 53, 57, 59; *d.* 51, 55, 59

Dipper, Big. *See* Big Dipper

Dipper, Little. *See* Little Dipper

"Dog days," 97-98

Dog Star. *See* Sirius

Dolphin. *See* Job's Coffin

Double stars: first observed, 4; Gamma Andromedae, 40; in Leo, 67; Mizar and Alcor, 4

Draco (drā'kō) the Dragon: appearance and location, 15; *d.* 16; legends, 17-18; size, 78

Dwarf stars, 74-75; Proxima Centauri as, 96-97

Eagle. *See* Aquila

Earth: appearance from other planets, 102-103; atmosphere, 112; axis, 9, 153; curvature, *p.* 112; gravity, 112; length of year, 110, 112; location in space, 49; orbit around sun, 7-8, 48, 67-69, 103, 105, 110, 112, 113, 125, 131-32, 163-64, 166; *d.* 68, 104, 131; origin, 161-62; *d.* 161; phases as seen from moon, 139; rotation, 7, 112, 118, 155-56, 159, 163-64; size, 112; *d.* 112; temperature, 111, 149-50

Easter, date of, 165

Eclipses: of moon, 146-48; *d.* 147; of sun, 145-46, 157-58; *d.* 146, *p.* 157

Ecliptic: definition of, 69, 163

Egyptian belief concerning Sirius, 97

Electra, 83-84

Equator, Celestial. *See* Celestial Equator

Eros, 126

Eurydice (û-rĭd'ĭ-sē), 53-54, 56

Evening Star. *See* Venus

Field-glass views. *See* opera-glass views

First-magnitude stars, 19-20; list of, 101

Fluorescence, 90, 93

"Flying saucers," 109

Fomalhaut (fō'mûl-hôt), brightness, 80, 101; color, 101; distance, 101; location, 80; *d.* 80; when to look for, 80

"Four Stars." *See* Southern Cross

Galaxies, 47, 49; *d.* 48; Andromeda Nebula largest known, 49

Galaxy, our: center of, 47, 63, 78; Herschel's picture of, 45-46; modern picture of, 46-49; *d.* 46, 47; number of stars in, 46, 48; our location in, 46, 47; *d.* 46, 47; shape of, 45-46, 48; *d.* 46, 47;

size, 48-49; star clusters in, 47, 63

Galileo, 118, 150

Gemini (jĕm'ĭ-nī) the Twins: appearance and location, 100; *d.* 100; in zodiac, *d.* 68; patrons of navigation, 99-100

George III, King, 122

Golden Fleece, 18

Good Shepherd. *See* Auriga

Gorgon Medusa (gôr'gŭn mĕ-dū'sȧ), 33-35, 38, 41

Gravity: on the earth, 112; on Mercury, 107

Great Bear. *See* Big Dipper

Great Orion Nebula: appearance, 90; *p.* 88; color, 90, 93; gas near hot stars, 90, 93; location, 87, 90

Great Spiral Nebula in Andromeda: appearance, 43, 45; *p.* 44; as galaxy, 47, 49; distance, 43, 44; Herschel's studies of, 45, 47; location, *d.* 37, 39; size, 43, 49

Greek alphabet: used in naming stars, 24-25

Greek legends. *See* Andromeda; Berenice's Hair; Big Dipper; Boötes; Cassiopeia; Cepheus; Cygnus; Draco; Gemini; Hercules; Leo; Little Dipper; Lyra; Northern Crown; Orion; Pegasus; Perseus; Pleiades; Procyon; Royal Family of the Sky; Scorpius; Virgo

Guardians of the Pole, 15

Halley's Comet: appearance, *p.* 127; orbit, 129; *d.* 128; portent of disaster, 129; present location of, 129

Hebrew legends: Auriga, 85; Job's Coffin, 60; Leo, 66

Hercules (hûr'kŭ-lēz): appearance and location, 62; *d.* 61, 62; legend, 61, 66; star cluster in, 62-63, 65; *d.* 61; *p.* 63

Hercules star cluster: appearance, 63, 65; *p.* 63; compared with Manger, 70; conditions in, 65; location, *d.* 61; once considered nebula, 92

Herdsman. *See* Boötes

Herschel, Sir William: discovery of Uranus, 121-22; picture of our galaxy, 45-46, 122; studies of nebulae, 45, 47; studies of star clusters, 45, 63; telescope maker, 45, 121-22

Hesperides (hĕs-pĕr'ŭ-dēz), 18

Hesperus (hĕs'pĕr-ŭs). *See* Venus

Horoscope writers, 69

"Horse and rider." *See* Alcor; Mizar

Hunter. *See* Orion

Hyades. *See* Taurus

Indian legends. *See* American Indian legends

International Date Line, 168

Island universes. *See* Galaxies

Jason, 18

Job, 59-60, 94

Job's Coffin: appearance and location, 59; *d.* 59; legend, 59-60

Juno (jōō'nō), 17

Jupiter (jōō'pŭ-tēr) (god), 17-18, 33, 35, 83, 99, 116

Jupiter (planet): appearance, 117, 118; *p.* 117; atmosphere, 119, 122-23; brightness, 109, 114, 117-18; color, 117; family of comets, 129; length of "year," 116; life on, 119; orbit around sun, 116, 117, 129; *d.* 104; rotation, 116, 118; satellites, 116, 118; size, 116-17; *d.* 116; temperature, 117, 119

Kant, Immanuel, 162

Kids. *See* Auriga

Kuiper, Gerard P., 114, 123, 124, 162

Latitude, estimating from altitude of Polaris, 11

Legends. *See* American Indian legends; Greek legends; Hebrew legends

Leo the Lion: appearance and location, 66, 69; *d.* 67; in zodiac, 67; *d.* 68; double star in, 67; legends, 66; radiant of meteor shower in, 133; sun "in," 67, 69

Leonid meteors: good displays of, 134; shower in 1833, 134; when observed, 133

Leverrier (lĕ-vĕ'ryā'), Urbain J. J., 123-24

Libra (lī'brȧ): in zodiac, *d.* 68; date sun "enters," 69

Light: how stars radiate, 73; of moon, 102; of planets, 102; of nebulae, 90; of ring nebula in Lyra, 56-57, 90; speed of, 22, 48

Light-year, 21-22

178

Rigel (rī'jŭl) : brightness, 93, 101; color, 93, 101; distance, 101; legend, 93; location, 93; d. 92; temperature, 93

Ring Nebula, 56-57, 90

Roman view of meteorites, 137

Rotation: of celestial sphere, 9, 164; of earth, 7, 112, 118, 155-56, 159, 163-64; of Jupiter, 116, 118; of Mars, 113; of Mercury, 106; of moon, 149; of planets, 105; of Neptune, 123, 124; of Pluto, 124; of Saturn, 119; of sun, 159; of Uranus, 121; of Venus, 111

"Royal Family of the Sky," 31-35, 40; d. 37

Sagittarius (săj'ĭ-tā'rĭ-ŭs) the Archer: appearance and location, 75-76, 78; d. 75, 76, 78, 79; in zodiac, d. 68; dark clouds in Milky Way in, p. 91; star cloud in, p. 77

Sahara Desert, legend, 72

St. Paul, 99-100

Satellites, 106; Galilean, 118; of earth, 112; of Jupiter, 116, 118; of Mars, 113, 114; of Neptune, 122; p. 122; of Saturn, 119; p. 120; of Uranus, 121; p. 121

Saturn: appearance, 119, 120; p. 120; color, 120; density, 120; length of "year," 119; life on, 120; orbit around sun, 119, 120; d. 104; rings, 119; p. 120; rotation, 119; satellites, 119; size, 119; d. 119; temperature, 120

Scorpius (skôr'pĭ-ŭs) the Scorpion: appearance and location, 71, 75, 78, 96; d. 71, 78, 79; in zodiac, d. 68; legend, 71-72

Sea nymphs, 33, 34, 35

"Seas" on moon, 150; p. 152

Seasons, cause of: 153-56; d. 154, 155

Serpens (sûr'pĕnz) : appearance and location, 78; d. 79

Serviss, Garrett P., 65

Shapley, Harlow, 46-47, 63

Shooting stars. See Meteors

Sidereal day, 165

Sidereal year, 165

Sirius (sĭr'ĭ-ŭs) : and "dog days," 98; as Dog Star, 97; as Nile Star, 97; brightness, 94, 96, 97, 101, 109; color, 96, 97, 101; distance, 97, 101; dwarf companion,

74; location, 94, 97, 99; d. 95, 98, 99; rate of approach to earth, 97; temperature, 97

Solar day, 165-66

Solar system, 48; origin of, 161-62; d. 161

South celestial pole, 17, 163; d. 164

Southern Cross, 58

Southern Fish, 80; d. 80

Spica (spī'kå) : brightness, 28, 101; color, 28, 72, 101; distance, 101; location, 28, 29, 65; d. 28, 29, 64; meaning of word, 29; temperature, 72

Square of Pegasus. See Pegasus

Standard time, 167-68; zones of the United States, d. 169

Star cloud in Sagittarius, 78; p. 77

Star clusters: Berenice's Hair, 65; d. 64, 67; in Hercules, 62-63, 65; d. 61; p. 63; Manger, 69-70; d. 67, 98; number, 63; once considered nebulae, 45, 63, 92; Pleiades, 81-83, 90; d. 81, 84, 95; p. 82; use in locating galaxy center, 47, 63

Stars: apparent brightness, 20, 41-42, 72; apparent daily motions of, 7, 11; p. 10; appearance through telescope, 93, 102; burnt-out, 75; colors, 72, 101; clusters of, see Star clusters; distances, 4, 21, 41-42, 101; dwarf, 74-75; fixed, 4; Greek letters used to designate, 24-25; individual motions of, 4, 5, 52; magnitudes, 20; novae, 42-43; number in our galaxy, 46, 48; number in Milky Way, 45, 46; number visible, 20, 65; origin of, 73; radiation of, 73; "second childhood" of, 74-75; sizes, 4, 20, 21, 72-73; stages of growth, 73-75; temperatures, 72-73; true brightness, 41-42, 72-73; twinkling of, 96, 102; types, 73-75; variable, 41-42

Stetson, Harlan T., xiv

Summer Triangle: appearance, 50, 51, 99; d. 51, 59; location, 51

Sun: age, 161; apparent daily path, 163-64; apparent yearly path among stars, 67-69, 103, 163-64, 165; d. 68; appearance from Neptune, 124; appearance from other stars, 21; as radio-broadcaster, 57; atmosphere, 158; brightness, 71; corona, 157-58;

MAP OF NORTHERN STARS. Stars that you will see in the sky as you face north. Turn the map so that the proper month is at the bottom: then the stars just above the name of that month will be due north—just above the horizon at 9 P.M.